EATING for Healthy LIVING

Marshall Cavendish

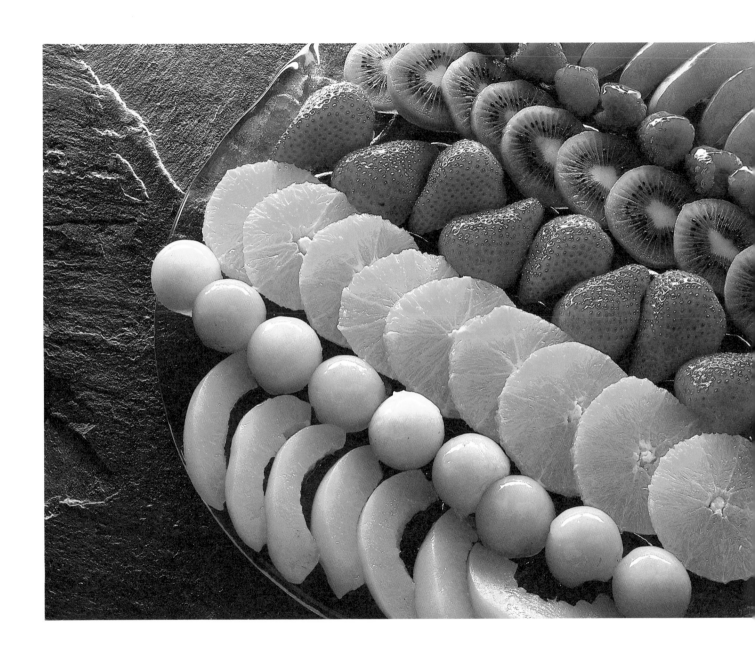

Nutritionist: Hazel Billson
Editor: Sally Taylor
Designer: Rupert Day
Production: Richard Churchill

Published by Marshall Cavendish Books Limited
58 Old Compton Street London W1V 5PA

ISBN 0-86307485 5

CONTENTS

nutrition

All sorts of things contribute to our good health – or lack of it – at any one time, and eating a healthy diet is one of the most important factors of all. As our understanding of the relationship of diet to health is continually increasing, we know that not only does eating well contribute to a state of good health and well-being, but it can also do wonders for the morale and the physique. Eating well, however, does not mean eating to excess. The problems of over-nutrition, leading to obesity are all too apparent in appearance, but they bring, too, a mass of attendant health problems. Somehow they are rendered all the more undesirable when viewed against the desperate plight of the under-nourished and starving, a plight of which we are all now only too aware.

Most of us are in the fortunate position of having plenty of foods to choose from, so some knowledge of food values is a help in choosing a healthy diet for us and our families. A balanced diet should contain all the vital nutrients which the body requires to function efficiently and these are proteins, carbohydrates, fats, vitamins and minerals. The role of these, and foods in which they may be found is summarised in the nutrition chart on page 7.

Provided that the daily diet includes protein-containing foods, some milk or dairy foods, staple foods such as bread, potatoes and cereals, and fruit and vegetables, there is no need to worry about eating a specific food for each of the vitamins and nutrients. These 'everyday' foods are all good sources of vitamins and minerals. But a balanced diet need not, and indeed should not, consist of the same foods every day. Eating a variety of foods over a period of days from each of the groups mentioned will ensure an adequate intake of all nutrients, as well as being more palatable and satisfying because it is varied. For example, although liver is a very good source of protein, iron and vitamins, few people would wish to eat it every day; incorporate it once a week into the diet and hopefully, it will be greeted with enthusiasm.

Foods must also supply us with energy for warmth and activity as well as for the internal functions of the body. Virtually all foods and drinks supply energy and this is measured in

calories or kilojoules – units in which the energy that the body requires is also measured. The diet must contain sufficient energy for weight maintenance and to allow for growth in the case of children and pregnant women. If the diet contains more energy than the body requires, or can burn off as heat, then the excess energy will be stored as fat; overweight and obesity are the next stage.

It is true to say that the body could obtain all the energy it needed, and indeed more, from a diet consisting wholly of biscuits and chocolate bars, for example; but it would be lacking in many other nutrients and would not remain healthy for long. It is therefore sensible to choose foods for energy which

are also good sources of nutrients and to eat sparingly of the foods which only supply energy and little else. Prime examples of these 'rogue' foods are sugars, fats and alcohol.

Many studies into diet and health have linked diets which are high in fat, sugar and salt and low in fibre with numbers of illnesses ranging from constipation to heart disease. Consequently, modern recommendations are for diets high in fibre, low in fat (especially saturated fats), low in sugar and low in salt. If this sounds rather daunting and complicated don't worry: many general recommend-ations can be made to help you to achieve this type of diet without undue planning or research. Let us look at each of these in turn.

constipation. Some types of fibre also have a beneficial effect on the blood.

To increase the fibre intake in your diet, use wholemeal bread in preference to other types and eat at least three slices a day. Also try to include a wholegrain cereal, such as oats or muesli or some manufactured cereal made with the whole of the wheat. Include two helpings of vegetables and two portions of fruit per day. Substitute brown rice for white, wholemeal pasta for white pasta and if you must eat biscuits, choose those containing fibre, such as digestive biscuits, rather than those made with white flour. Experiment with using wholemeal flour in cooking or, if the transition seems too drastic all at once, begin by using a mixture of wholemeal flour and white flour.

Snacks which are high in fibre include dried fruit and nuts, fresh fruit and individually-packed snack bars made with oats and seeds. As an added bonus, many foods which are high in fibre are also higher in vitamins and minerals than their more refined counterparts.

fats

Some of the fat in our daily diet is provided by such obvious sources as butter and margarine, by various cooking fats such as lard and by oils, but more is 'hidden' in other foods – meat, cheese, pastries, biscuits, milk, cream and foods which have fat used in their manufacture, such as chocolate. Fats contribute a great deal of energy or calories to the diet; each gram of fat provides approximately 9 kcal/38 kJ. Eating too much fat is thus an easy way to become overweight, while an excess of fat in the diet may also be associated with an increased risk of heart disease and various other illnesses.

The difference between the different types of fat can seem rather confusing to someone who is anxious to choose wisely. Terms such as saturated and polyunsaturated seem to be bandied about without the back-up information we sometimes feel we need. Putting it simply, it is saturated fats that are the ones believed to be the most detrimental and they are therefore the ones to be treated with the most caution. By and large, animal fats – meats and dairy products – as well as hard fats such as lard and hard margarine contain more saturated fat than polyunsaturated fats. By decreasing your intake of these foods then, you will reduce the fat overall in your diet, whilst significantly

lowering the amount of saturated fats. In practice, this means eating less meat and more meals based on fish, poultry and pulses or beans; it means reducing the amount of spreading fat such as butter (try limiting yourself to 100g/4oz per week) and using less high-fat cheeses and cream. Limit, too, the amount of full-fat milk you drink to about 300 ml/$\frac{1}{2}$ pint per day (bear in mind its use in cooking – not just the amount you pour on your cereal or drink in cups of tea and coffee) and use one of the reduced-fat milks for any milk over this amount.

Try to reduce the amount of fat you use in your everyday cooking; the recipes in this book concentrate on low-fat ingredients in the main and they use minimal fat in preparation. Do not be tempted to use more simply because you usually do; the amount stated in the recipes is quite sufficient. Additional information on reducing fat is given later on, but as a further pointer, reduce your intake of fried foods, especially those which have been deep-fried and beware of those hidden fats in pastries, biscuits, cakes and crisp-type snacks.

sugar

Sugar in many forms is added to a high percentage of manufactured foods. Although we undoubtedly enjoy its sweet taste, it is wise to remember that it does not supply any nutrients, apart from calories and these would be better obtained from other foods. Foods which contain sugar – sweets, biscuits, sweet drinks – are all too often eaten in large quantities because of their palatability, certainly, but also because they are readily available as convenience foods. And foods high in sugar are often high in fat too; cakes, chocolate and sweet pastries are all instances.

Because of its convenience and popularity, sugar may displace other more nutritious foods in the diet, either by spoiling the appetite, which happens when sugary foods are eaten as snacks, or by supplying a sufficient amount of energy at the expense of those foods which are high in fibre. Sugar is traditionally associated with overweight, but it is not just a problem for those who fight a daily battle with the scales: apart from its association with obesity, sugar is primarily responsible for tooth decay – a serious problem amongst both children and adults. (Incidentally, bad teeth or poorly fitting dentures can result in a badly limited diet).

fibre

This may also be referred to as roughage and is found only in foods of vegetable, rather than animal, origin. There are several types of fibre but they all comprise that part of food which remains undigested and is therefore ultimately excreted. While inside the body, however, fibre has some important roles: it adds to a feeling of fullness after a meal which can be important in preventing over-eating, it helps food to pass smoothly through the digestive system, and it enables waste products to be eliminated from the body without discomfort by alleviating

The logical procedure, as far as sugar in the diet is concerned then, is to reduce the quantity as much as you can to make way for more nourishing foods. If you crave sweetness in your diet, turn to nature for it; she provides her own natural sweetness in fresh fruit, and even more so in dried fruits, and also in some vegetables – carrots and parsnips for example.

Ways to reduce the sugar intake include cutting sugar out of drinks and avoiding sweet drinks and 'pops', cutting down on sweets and chocolates (restrict yourself to once a week if you are particularly addicted) and using less sugar in baking and cooking – many recipes do not need nearly as much sugar as is given. Lots of fruits are now canned without sugar and are far better for you than those in heavy syrups; it is also possible to buy breakfast cereals without sugar. The only way to avoid sugar in many manufactured products is simply to avoid using the product and use fresh ingredients instead. Sugar between meals in the form of sweets is particularly bad for the teeth; if you must nibble – and many of us must – try some of the snacks suggested in the section on fibre, and drink sugar-free drinks, fresh fruit juices or water.

Lest this sounds like a counsel of real deprivation, it is not necessary to avoid every last grain of sugar. Just try to think of it as a condiment to be used sparingly to bring out the flavour of foods, rather than as a food in itself. Just remember that a healthy diet should not contain too much sugar of any type; brown sugars contain just as many calories as white sugar and are just as detrimental to teeth, although they can be useful for providing flavour as well as sweetness. Honey, treacle and molasses are also high in calories, so use them guardedly.

salt

This is another food which has come under investigation for its possible bad effect on health: as a result the recommendation is to use less of it. In addition to the salt used in cooking (which in fact is probably about all we should use), many people then sprinkle salt and/or salty sauces over their food. A factor to bear in mind is that many manufactured foods are already very high in salt – for example, smoked foods, cheeses, canned meats and vegetables, snack foods such as crisps and roasted salted nuts, as well as instant dried foods. Use more fresh foods

and you will effectively reduce your salt intake, then try not to add it to foods at the table and use less in cooking; flavour with herbs and spices instead – the taste is better and so is the health effect.

The conclusion to be reached from the above guidelines must surely be that the optimum diet for health will consist mainly of wholefoods – and wholefoods are those that are as near as possible to their natural state. Eating a wholefood diet benefits health certainly and also improves the condition of the skin and hair as well as mental and emotional health. This it does by supplying a steady stream of the nutrients the body requires for efficient functioning.

Eating a wholefood diet is also a recommended way to lose weight, as the energy content of the diet can be reduced without compromising the intake of essential nutrients. This can be achieved by cutting out sugar altogether, choosing protein foods that are low in fat and calories such as poultry, fish, low-fat cheese, and skimmed milk, eating controlled quantities of wholemeal bread, cereals and pulses, plus plenty of fruit and vegetables to add bulk to the diet. It is almost as easy as it sounds! In addition this type of diet will be much more healthy and effective in the long-term than crash dieting or low carbohydrate diets which actually deprive the body of vital nutrients and probably lead to cravings. It is worth stressing again that being overweight is not primarily undesirable from an appearance point of view; it is fundamentally detrimental to good health, and for this reason, should not be lightly dismissed. Your doctor will be able to advise you if you should lose weight.

Eating a wholefood diet can be helpful in stabilising a steady weight and for those with compulsive eating problems, it can help in forming better, regular eating habits. For those people who need to gain weight, a wholefood diet is the healthy way to do so.

NUTRITION CHART

Nutrient	Functions	Sources
Carbohydrates	Provide energy. Excess is stored as fat.	Sugar, bread and cereals. Potatoes, root vegetables and fruits. Milk, biscuits and cakes.
Proteins	Body growth and repair. Excess is used as energy and will be stored as fat.	Meat, fish, eggs, cheese and milk. Beans and pulses, nuts, bread and cereals. Potatoes.
Fats	Provide energy. Excess is stored as fat.	Butter, margarine and oils. Meat, cheese, oily fish and nuts.
Iron	Necessary for red blood cells and muscles.	Meat and offal. Beans and pulses, dark green vegetables, bread and cereals. Eggs.
Calcium	Formation of bones and teeth.	Milk, yoghurt and cheese. Bread and fish bones.
Phosphorus	Present throughout the body, especially bones and teeth.	Present in nearly all foods.
Magnesium	Present in bones and all body cells.	Some in most foods, especially in vegetables.
Vitamin A	Essential for vision. Promotes healthy skin.	Fish oils, liver and kidney. Milk and eggs. Dark green and orange vegetables.
Vitamin D	Bone formation.	Oily fish, eggs and margarine. Also the action of sunlight on the skin.
Vitamin B_1 (Thiamin)	Release of energy.	Whole grain cereals and fortified breakfast cereals. Pork, offal and eggs.
Vitamin B_2 (Riboflavin)	For the use of energy from food.	Fortified breakfast cereals and wholegrains. Milk and liver.
Nicotinic acid	For the use of energy from food.	Fortified breakfast cereals and bread. Potatoes and peas. Liver.
Vitamin B_6 (Pyridoxine)	For protein metabolism and formation of red blood cells.	Meat, fish and eggs, wholegrain cereals.
Vitamin B_{12}	Formation of cells.	Only in animal products, especially liver.
Folic acid	Formation of cells.	Offal, raw leafy green vegetables, pulses, oranges and bananas. Bread. Offal.
Vitamin C	Maintenance of healthy connective tissue.	Fruit and vegetables especially citrus fruits and potatoes.
Vitamin E	As an antioxidant.	Wholegrain cereals, eggs and vegetable oils.
Vitamin K	Clotting of the blood.	Spinach, cabbage and peas. Cereals. It is also synthesized in the body.

planning the day's meals

Aim to eat at regular times through the day, and don't miss out breakfast. The body functions more efficiently on moderately-sized regular meals than it does on snacky bits and pieces with a massive meal at the end of the day. At each meal, try to include some protein-containing food, whether of animal or vegetable origin, some carbohydrate (not sugar) – preferably unrefined, and some fruit or vegetables. A little sugar and/or fat may also be included, although those who are trying to slim should avoid the sugar, and may substitute a low-fat spread.

Introduce variety at breakfast by varying cereals, breads and fruits, or by adding something simply cooked such as an egg and some well-grilled bacon or grilled tomatoes and baked beans (see page 55).

For light lunches or evening snacks, there are any number of foods to choose from and you will find all sorts of tasty ideas on the pages that follow. For taking with you to work, sandwiches and salads are ideal, but choose wholemeal bread and low-fat fillings for sandwiches – lean meat, chicken (without the skin), canned fish, low-fat cheese or egg and add plenty of salad ingredients to the filling. Salads are easily transportable and here the variations are infinite, with lots of ideas in this book. Finish up the light meal with some fresh fruit.

If you choose to buy sandwiches on your way to work or when you are out, look for a sandwich bar that makes its sandwiches with wholemeal bread. If the ones near you do not do this as a matter of course, suggest that they do! A salad sandwich followed by a yoghurt – preferably a natural one – will have a good balance of protein and other nutrients. If you are buying a salad snack rather than making your own, avoid those that are drowning in a sea of mayonnaise or other oily dressing; salads like this contain more fat than a portion of chips.

If you eat out regularly at restaurants as part of your daily life, or if you eat in a canteen at work, do choose very carefully. Go for plain foods that are simply cooked such as grilled or roast meat and especially avoid fatty sauces and stews. Grilled fish is wonderful (fried fish is not) as is simply cooked shellfish. Plain boiled potatoes or baked potatoes are good choices, but if they are not available try a variety of vegetables or a salad – and ask for a salad to be served without dressing. It is currently quite rare to find wholemeal pasta or brown rice on the menu, but you may be able to get wholemeal bread to accompany the meal. For dessert, look for seasonal fresh fruits or fruit salads; (you may find fruit in the starter menu), or a light dessert such as sorbet. Alternatively, opt for cheese (and biscuits if you must), but make it a small piece of cheese; it is quality, not quantity, that counts.

For your main meals, choose dishes that balance out the rest of the day's intake in terms of calories and protein, do include fresh vegetables and fruit. Particularly if your other meals have been hurried, relax over your main meal; digestion is not helped by gulped-down meals, nor do you feel as satisfied after a meal eaten at speed as one taken at a leisurely pace.

If these suggestions – both about the sorts of foods and the quantities you should be eating and the organisation of your daily intake of food – comprise fundamental changes in your eating patterns, although the indication is that change is long due, it may be too much to make it all at once. Instead make a few changes at a time, beginning by increasing the fibre in your diet. Then the next week make an effort to reduce your fat intake, and so on.

drinks

There is no getting away from the fact that a heavy intake of alcohol is not compatible with health. However, although it provides negligible amounts of nutrients, there is no reason why it should not be used – sparingly.

Tea and coffee also contain negligible amounts of nutrients, but are popular and refreshing drinks that are harmless provided they are not drunk in huge quantities. You may like to try decaffeinated drinks, grain coffees and herbal teas for a change; these are free of stimulants. Other healthy drinks are fruit and vegetable juices and water, bottled or from the tap.

shopping for healthy food

what to look for

Making and using a shopping list is always useful when buying food, particularly if you are working to a tight budget or shopping for a large number of people when it becomes all too easy to forget important items. Thinking ahead about meals may seem time-consuming, but it enables you to plan healthy, balanced menus and actually saves time wondering what to buy when you are out shopping. Aim to base meals around foods that are in season.

meat

Meat is a good source of protein, iron and vitamins, but it can also supply an excess of fat to the diet. Look for lean meat; it may be more expensive than fattier cuts, but it will require less trimming and less will be required for a satisfying portion. 100 g/4 oz lean raw meat per person will provide ample protein in a meal and it can be bulked out as required with fibre-containing vegetables or cereals.

In a supermarket, you will probably be able to examine a pack of meat to see how much fat it contains. If you buy your meat from a butcher, find a reliable one who will sell you non-fatty meat. Wherever you buy it, it is easier to trim fat from the meat which has a rim of fat around the flesh such as lamb cutlets or good steak, than from meat which is layered or marbled with fat, such as belly of pork or minced beef. If you do buy a fattier meat, cook it using a moist method where the dish can be cooled after cooking and the fat skimmed off before reheating.

Cheaper cuts of meat will be as nutritious as more expensive cuts and most butchers are happy to advise on how to cook less familiar cuts. Offal, especially liver and kidney, can make an extremely useful contribution to the diet and it is a good idea to include as many types regularly as you can persuade your family to eat. Those who do not like the strong flavour of ox or lambs' liver, may find the milder flavour of chicken liver quite acceptable, or be prepared to eat liver 'disguised' as pâté.

Poultry is a good source of protein that contains less fat than red meats (except in the skin). There will be little nutritional difference between frozen or fresh poultry, but the latter will have more flavour. Try to buy the giblets with a whole chicken or duck; they are useful for adding to vegetables to make a good-flavoured stock.

Canned and processed meats such as sausages, beefburgers and meat pies are generally prepared with a great deal of salt and other additives so should not be used often in a wholefood diet. Small quantities of bacon and delicatessen sausages, however, can be useful to add flavour to other dishes such as soups and pulse recipes. Canned meat, such as corned beef or ham, is a useful storecupboard item when shopping for fresh foods is not possible for any reason. Popular foods – beefburgers and fish cakes for example – can easily be made at home using fresh ingredients, and will have far more flavour and less additives than their mass-produced counterparts.

fish

All types of fish are a good choice in a wholefood diet, as they are rich sources of protein and minerals. White fish is low in fat and calories, while oily fish is low in saturated fat and provides vitamins A and D. Really fresh fish (if you can get it) will have more flavour than most frozen fish. Whenever you can, choose a mixture of types according to their seasonal availability and your own taste. If you can only obtain frozen fish, its flavour can be enhanced by the use of a well-flavoured sauce, or fresh herbs. Bear in mind that smoked fish has a high salt content, so its use should be limited. Generally its strong flavour means smaller amounts than fresh fish are sufficient.

The use of canned fish increases the varieties available and most are without additives (check the can for this). The soft bones in sardines and canned salmon can be crushed in with the flesh and are excellent sources of calcium and phosphorus. Buy a variety of canned fish to keep in the storecupboard for quick meals and snacks.

dairy products

All milk and milk products, apart from cream, are high in calcium and phosphorus as well as protein and should be included daily in the diet. However there is a rather bewildering number of different milks available from both milkmen and supermarkets and you might have some difficulty in choosing. To help you, pasteurized and homogenized milk contain more of some vitamins than UHT or sterilized milk, but the chief difference between milks is in their fat content. Jersey and Guernsey milk contains more fat than standard pasteurized or homogenized. Semi-skimmed milk has some fat removed and skimmed milk has had all fat removed. You may like to try using semi-skimmed milk for drinking and to pour on cereals and skimmed milk for cooking, as a way of reducing your fat intake. Young children should generally be given non-skimmed milk unless advised otherwise.

Skimmed milk does not contain the fat-soluble vitamins A and D, although these are sometimes added back into it, particularly in dried skimmed milk. If you are buying a dried skimmed milk and want a low-fat one, avoid those which have had vegetable fat added back – the so-called 'filled milks' – although these can be useful as a storecupboard item. Tinned milks such as evaporated and condensed milk are high in fat and/or sugar.

Cream is very high in fat, so use it sparingly. Buy the type with the least fat for the purpose you require – for example single cream for pouring, and whipping cream rather than double, for spooning and piping.

Yoghurt has become an enormously popular food in recent years, and it is extremely versatile. However, many types have sugar added to them, as well as a whole host of additives – among them extra fat in the form of cream. The best yoghurts to choose are those that are low in fat and have the shortest list of additives, preferably none at all, or perhaps just fruit and sugar. Study the labels carefully. The most useful type of yoghurt for cooking is natural yoghurt and this is also lowest in calories. If you use a lot of it, try making it at home.

When it comes to cheeses, there is an immense range to choose from, with varieties from many different countries. Cheese is high in protein but many sorts are also high in saturated fats so should be treated with caution. If you like cheese and cheese dishes, choose a mixture of low-fat cheeses such as curd and cottage cheese as well as the high-fat hard cheeses which generally give more flavour. To this end, too, buy mature cheeses for cooking, although they cost more than milder cheese you will need to use less to give a strong flavour to a cooked dish and you thereby reduce the overall amount of fat. (A similar effect can be obtained by allowing mild cheeses to ripen and then using them for cooking.)

A number of hard reduced-fat cheeses are available now and you may like to use these both for cooking or for eating with biscuits as a snack. Other cheeses which are low in fat and calories include Ricotta, Fromage Blanc, Quark and Fetta and these have all sorts of uses in everyday meal preparation.

An effective way to reduce the amount of fat in the diet is to use less spreading fat on your bread, toast, rolls and so on – whether butter or margarine. (Butter contains vitamins A and D naturally and margarine must have these vitamins added by law.) Low-fat spreads are available which have less fat and calories than butter or margarine, but some varieties are not suitable for cooking. It is probably advisable to avoid using hard saturated fats such as lard and suet and instead, use a margarine or oil which is high in polyunsaturated fat for cooking. Oils which are high in polyunsaturated fat include sunflower oil, safflower oil and soyabean oil. Incidentally oils do contain as much fat and therefore as many calories as butter and margarine but do not contain any vitamin A or D (although many are a good source of vitamin E).

Finally in dairy products, we come to eggs. When buying these, ensure that they are fresh by checking the packing date on the box. There appears to be little difference in the nutritional value of an egg from a battery hen or one from a free-range hen, although you may prefer the latter for its flavour. There is, of course, no difference in the nutritional value between white and brown shelled eggs.

fruit and vegetables

If you do not grow your own fruit and vegetables, then a good market or greengrocer is the next best option to obtain really fresh produce. Fruits and vegetables are invaluable in the diet as a source of vitamins, minerals and fibre as well as for taste and variety. Use as many different types as you can, especially those which are in season and make sure that they look fresh; those which are old and withering will have a diminished vitamin content. If possible, buy fruit and vegetables at least twice a week so that they are really fresh.

Supermarkets vary in the quality of their fruit and vegetables. Many will now allow you to pick out your own purchases so that you can check the quality as well as buying just the quantity you require. It is usually worth paying a little extra for good quality produce; cheaper over-ripe items will often get wasted if not used immediately.

Organically grown produce which has not been treated with any chemicals may become more widely available in the future. Until that time, fruit and vegetables should always be thoroughly washed before consumption, particularly if they are to be eaten raw.

Contrary to what you might think, frozen fruit and vegetables are of high nutritional quality and are extremely useful for convenience. They may even be more economical at certain times of year when fresh produce is scarce, and of course there will be no wastage with them.

Canned fruits and vegetables have normally suffered some vitamin losses as a result of the necessary heating to a high temperature. Many – particularly fruit – are canned with heavy syrups or, in the case of vegetables, with high levels of salt. Look out for fruits canned in natural juices without added sugar and also vegetables canned without salt. Useful canned vegetables for a storecupboard are canned tomatoes, sweetcorn and a variety of beans and pulses.

Fresh herbs are also worth looking out for in greengrocers and supermarkets, although many can be grown very easily indoors. They can greatly add to the flavour and appearance of many meals.

bread

All breads are good sources of protein and vitamins, but wholemeal bread is strongly to be preferred for its high fibre and vitamin content. You may prefer to make your own bread (see chapter eight – Wholesome Baking) otherwise look around for varieties that you enjoy. It is possible to buy packaged varieties which are free of additives and often these have the best flavour.

provisions and dry goods

When buying any packaged goods, study the labels to see what they contain. Chemical additives are usually denoted by 'E' numbers; books and leaflets are available giving details of what all these additives are together with their possible effects on the body as well as on the food. For a natural diet try to avoid too many additives, although there is no need to be obsessional about avoiding every single one. Foods which are free of additives will have more natural flavour and colour. Lists of ingredients in packaged goods will be given in the respective order of amounts with the greatest amounts at the beginning. Avoid foods which contain long lists of ingredients especially if sugar or salt (or sodium) figures predominate. In this regard, check instant soups and puddings and packet mixes particularly carefully. (Jams and preserves will necessarily be an exception, as they contain a large amount of sugar.)

Many wholefoods are now available in supermarkets and grocers as well as in 'health food' shops. Commonly available wholefoods include wholemeal pasta of different varieties, brown rice, wholemeal flour (plain and self-raising) or 85% wholemeal flour if you prefer, many types of dried beans and pulses, dried fruits, nuts, breakfast cereals made with wholewheat, muesli without sugar, biscuits and crispbreads made with whole grains and unsweetened fruit juices. You may have a wholefood shop in your area where you can buy all of these, and other items, while also picking up advice about cooking unusual foods such as seaweeds. If you have any 'ethnic' shops nearby, look out for exotic vegetables, interesting spices and herbs, unusual sauces and canned foods which will add interest and variety to your healthy diet.

To summarise, the simple rules are – buy plenty of fresh foods, including fruits and vegetables and when buying manufactured foods, look for those that are high in fibre and low in fat, sugar, salt and chemical additives.

storing foods

How you store foods can play an important part in keeping them in good condition until you are ready to cook and eat them. Here are some simple guidelines.
- Store fresh fish and meat in a refrigerator, loosely covered on plates, to prevent drips. Use fish within 24 hours and meat within three days, and keep uncooked meat away from cooked meat.
- Store milk and other dairy produce in the refrigerator; eggs are an exception, they need only to be kept in a cool place. Cover cheese in cling film or foil to prevent it from drying out, but remove it from the refrigerator and allow it to come to room temperature for at least one hour before eating. Some soft cheeses – brie and camembert for example – are often better kept in a very cool place, rather than subjected to the chill of a refrigerator.
- Keep salad vegetables and soft fruits in the refrigerator. Apples, citrus fruits and pears can be kept in the refrigerator, or in brown paper bags in a cool place. Put them in a fruit bowl when you want to serve them rather than leaving them there all the time; they will deteriorate much more quickly if kept at room temperature. Bananas should not be kept in the refrigerator, incidentally; it will turn the skins brown very quickly.
- Keep green leafy vegetables in brown paper bags and use them as soon as possible; they will turn yellow in two to three days. Store potatoes and other root vegetables in bags away from the light and they will keep for several days; potatoes will keep for months.

Many packaged goods now give advice on the label as to when they should be used; consult these. However, all such goods should be kept in a dry place, away from direct light and should be used before too long. Canned goods will keep almost indefinitely.

If you have a freezer you will be able to keep a variety of meats, fish, fruit and vegetables, as well as made-up dishes. Many meals can be made in larger quantities and the remainder frozen for use at a later date.

Do remember to label and date packages for the freezer; one foil wrapped package soon looks like all the others. And remember, too, that frozen foods still have a limited life – they will not keep for ever. Fish in particular should be used after two to three months, and meat should not be kept for much longer. Fruit and vegetables will last a little longer, but are best used within six months.

storecupboard

Keep a storecupboard of items that enable you to whip up quick meals or meals for unexpected guests, as well as a stock of basic goods for cooking. Items for a storecupboard might include:
- Variety of canned fish e.g. salmon, tuna, sardines, anchovies, prawns and crab.
- Canned fruit in natural juice e.g. pineapple, peaches and mandarins.
- Dried skimmed milk.
- Wholemeal pasta in a variety of shapes, e.g. macaroni, spaghetti and twists or bows.
- Brown rice and short-grain rice for puddings.
- Wholemeal flour.
- Canned tomatoes and canned sweetcorn.
- Variety of dried herbs and spices (but use them fairly quickly; they lose their flavour if kept endlessly).
- Dried fruit.
- Nuts, including dessicated coconut and peanut butter.
- Salt and pepper.
- Wholemeal crackers and cheese biscuits
- Digestive biscuits (for cooking and eating).
- Parmesan cheese, grated for sprinkling on dishes.
- Lemon juice, vinegar, olive oil, or other oil, for salads.
- Yeast extract for flavouring.
- Sugar and honey.
- Jam, or other preserves.
- Gelatine for puddings.
- Cornflour for sauces.

preparing and cooking foods

The way in which foods are prepared and cooked can make a substantial difference to their contribution to a healthy diet. A fresh fillet of haddock, for example, full of protein and low in fat is wonderful grilled, but quite a different story if dipped in yellow-coloured starchy batter and fried in over-used oil.

When planning meals and preparing and cooking foods, remember again that you are aiming to produce meals high in fibre and low in fat, sugar and salt.

raw foods and salads

Try to include plenty of uncooked food in your day-to-day diet; salads are not just for slimmers – all contain some fibre and many are high in it. Salads may consist solely of raw foods – combinations of vegetables, fruits, nuts, seeds and other items or they may be composed of a mixture of raw and cooked ingredients. Use foods that are at a peak of freshness if eating raw and always wash them well to remove any traces of chemicals. Do not peel the skin where possible – on potatoes, carrots and apples for example – it is a rich source of fibre. In potatoes, much of the protein is also stored close to the skin and will thus be wasted if they are thickly peeled. A hard scrubbing brush enables you to clean vegetables sufficiently to make it unnecessary to remove the skin.

If possible, try not to prepare salads too far in advance of eating them as chopping fruits and vegetables can speed up the loss of vitamin C. Also many items will start to brown and become soft and unappetising quickly after chopping. Be sparing with the fat (oils) in dressings added to salads; many tasty dressings can be made using natural yoghurt as a base rather than mayonnaise. If you are going to add oil or French dressing, add only sufficient just to moisten the salad ingredients. An excess of dressing will disguise the food it is supposed to be complementing. You may like to try the reduced-fat salad creams and mayonnaises now available, but note that these are *reduced* in calories, not necessarily *low* in them.

A popular way of eating raw vegetables is as crudités, to be dipped into some kind of sauce or dip. This can be a danger area though; look for dips that are low in fat. It is also a good idea to keep some prepared raw vegetables in the refrigerator for when those hunger pangs strike. Button mushrooms, small tomatoes and scrubbed carrots and celery can all help to see you over a crisis.

The versatility of salads means they can be used for starters, side-salads, main courses, light lunches or desserts. Prepare fruit salads without adding sugar and dip fruits with a tendency to brown in lemon juice. Unsweetened fruit juices can be added to the prepared fruits to provide moisture and added flavour; extra fibre can be added in the form of dried fruits and/or nuts.

cooking meat

As mentioned before, meat should be trimmed of as much fat as possible before cooking. This may seem fiddly but the surplus fat will be of little use to your body, except to pad it with extra weight! A joint of meat can be roasted in a roasting bag or covered with foil to prevent it drying out, and should be basted simply with its own juices. Skim the meat juices before using them to make gravy or a sauce, as they will contain fat that melts out from the meat and this will rise to the surface. Meat for braising or stews does not need to be pre-browned in fat as most recipes instruct; in fact this will contribute little to the flavour and make little difference to the shrinking of the meat. Combine meat for stews and casseroles with plenty of vegetables or pulses to add fibre and bulk; and thus reduce the amount of meat needed.

If you need to fry meat, use a minimum of fat, preferably an oil low in saturated fat and a non-stick frying pan. This considerably cuts down the amount of fat needed, in fact you can often get away with using none at all.

Grilling is a good method of cooking meat as excess fat will drip out and can then be easily discarded. Beware of grilling under too ferocious a heat though, as this will dry out

the meat and make it tough.

Minced meat can be browned in a non-stick pan and the fat that comes out of it, poured off. Do this before you add chopped onions or other vegetables to the pan as they will quickly absorb the fat.

The majority of fat in poultry is in the skin, but do not attempt to remove the skin before roasting or grilling poultry or the flesh will become very dry. Instead remove it before serving. Where poultry is going to be cooked with other ingredients, or in a sauce, remove the skin before cooking.

cooking fish

Fish is usually best cooked as simply as possible. Oily fish can be grilled gently, or lightly sautéed in a tiny bit of fat: white fish can be steamed, poached in milk or stock, or stewed with other ingredients in a saucepan. Baking in the oven in a sauce or with vegetables wrapped in foil are methods suitable for all kinds of fish. Resist the temptation to deep-fry fish in batter or breadcrumbs; the coating will absorb a great deal of fat.

vegetarian dishes (dairy produce)

Eggs can be cooked in a number of ways without adding fat – such as poaching, boiling or baking. They can be scrambled in a non-stick pan with a little milk and without the addition of butter or cream; they will still taste rich and creamy. As we have seen, cheese dishes often tend to be high in fat so if using to flavour a sauce, use only enough cheese to give the sauce flavour (a little dry mustard helps to enhance the taste here). Make the sauce with low-fat ingredients such as skimmed milk and omit the fat, thickening the sauce just with flour. To make a cheesy topping for a dish, combine equal quantities of grated cheese and wholemeal breadcrumbs, to give less fat and more fibre. Do not use a cheese that goes stringy when heated and use mature or ripe cheeses which will decrease the quantities you require. A mere tablespoon of grated Parmesan will give a very cheesy flavour.

other vegetarian dishes

Nuts, although high in fibre are also high in fat, so try not to add extra fat to nutty recipes. Pulses and beans contain no fat at all, but plenty of fibre, so make dishes based on these ingredients a regular feature in your diet. Nearly all require overnight soaking if dried, so forward planning is essential.

sauces, gravies and soups

These are often very high in fat, especially if made by the 'roux' method or if they contain added cream. Use a minimum of fat for cooking ingredients such as onion, and where possible add home-made stock to make up the volume rather than using stock cubes and water or gravy flavouring, which are nearly always very high in salt. Alternatively look out for low-salt yeast extracts (available in health food shops and in some supermarkets) which are a useful flavouring ingredient. Saving liquid from cooking vegetables (keep in the refrigerator, but only for a day or two) will also be useful for flavouring.

Milky sauces can be made with skimmed milk, as also can 'cream' soups. Swirl a spoonful of yoghurt into these soups to give a creamy taste and appearance. For thickening soups, gravies and sauces, try using wholemeal flour mixed with a little water, stock or milk, and adding it slowly to the liquid, before bringing to the boil. Keep stirring until it thickens. If you object to the appearance of wholemeal flour in sauces, try adding cornflour; although this lacks fibre, it is easy to add as a thickener in the way

outlined above. Other thickening agents high in fibre include potato flour, oatmeal (for soups) and vegetable purées. Add extra fibre to soups by using barley, split peas, lentils and root vegetables.

Sweet sauces can also be made using skimmed milk and cornflour and flavoured with fruit juices, fruit zest and spices.

vegetables and accompaniments

Cooked vegetables to be served with a meal should be cooked very lightly; never overcooked, as this can result in a loss of vitamins. Steaming over boiling water is probably the best cooking method of all. When cooking green vegetables, add them to a small amount of boiling water, cover and cook until just tender, but still crisp. Try to avoid cooking vegetables too far in advance of eating, as they will lose vitamins while standing. Baking vegetables in the oven is a good way of using oven space if you are cooking another dish.

Potatoes can be cooked in many ways; choose the ones which do not require the addition of fat – baking and boiling – even steaming for small new potatoes. Potatoes, as with many other vegetables, will absorb lots of fat if given the chance.

Pasta and rice as an accompaniment should be cooked in plenty of boiling water, but not allowed to become soft or mushy. Wholemeal pasta and brown rice will take longer to cook than their refined counterparts; the time will vary a little according to type.

puddings and desserts

The main point to watch here – as you will know by now – is that you are not tempted to add too much sugar. Look for ways of reducing sugar in your favourite recipes or use artificial sweeteners. Base most of your sweet dishes on fruit to provide fibre, although if the main course has been fairly low in protein you may like to make a milky pudding or egg custard; again skimmed milk can be used. This book contains plenty of ideas for using yoghurt and low-fat cheeses rather than high-fat cream to produce creamy desserts.

baking

If you enjoy baking, experiment with using wholemeal flour in recipes for scones, pastry and cakes, but remember that most baked goods are high in fat, so should not be eaten too frequently. It is difficult to make pastry without using a high proportion of fat to flour, but if you enjoy pastry-based dishes roll it out very thinly and choose a low-fat filling such as cottage cheese and vegetables for a quiche, or stewed fruit sweetened with dried fruit for a dessert. Remember that dried fruit is useful when baking for providing sweetness as well as vitamins, iron and fibre. Fruit scones and tea-breads made with wholemeal flour can be healthy treats but if you really, really crave a slice of sticky chocolate cake, have it – just wait a few weeks before the next slice!

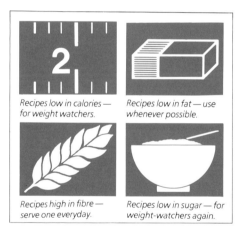

Recipes low in calories — for weight watchers.

Recipes low in fat — use whenever possible.

Recipes high in fibre — serve one everyday.

Recipes low in sugar — for weight-watchers again.

the recipes in this book

The recipes are designed to illustrate some of the points made in this introduction about foods for health and how to prepare them. They will quickly show you that healthy eating need never be boring or tasteless. the symbols at the top of the recipes are explained above. The time given at the top of each recipe is a guide for preparation and cooking combined. All the dishes are high in nutrients; for ideas on how to combine them in menus, turn to the menu planner on page 114-116.

slotted spoon and put them into a lightly greased ovenproof dish. Heat the oven to 190C/375F/Gas 5.

Heat 1 tablespoon oil in a frying-pan and fry the chopped onion for 5 minutes over a medium heat. Stir in the curry powder and red pepper and cook for a further 2 minutes. Remove from the heat and mix in the tomato purée, cooked rice, beef and chopped parsley. Season to taste.

Spoon this stuffing mixture into the onion shells and brush the shells lightly with the remaining oil. Cover the dish with foil and bake for 35-40 minutes, until the onions are tender when pierced with a sharp knife.

Serve with: Home-made tomato sauce and mashed potatoes.

Note: To cook brown rice, weigh out the required quantity and pour it into a measuring jug. Make a note of the volume, then tip it into a saucepan and add twice the quantity of boiling water or stock. Simmer very gently over a low heat for 35-40 minutes, until the grains are separate and softened. Add more boiling liquid towards the end of the cooking time if the rice is looking dry.

beef onions

1 hour + cooking rice

180 kcal/756 kJ per portion

Other varieties of cooked meat could be used instead of beef. For a vegetarian dish, substitute chopped mushrooms for the meat.

Serves 4

4 Spanish onions, peeled
salt and freshly ground black pepper
2 tablespoons oil
2 teaspoons mild curry powder
50 g/2 oz red pepper, finely diced
1 tablespoon tomato purée
100 g/4 oz cooked brown rice (40 g/1½ oz raw)
100 g/4 oz cooked lean beef, finely diced
1 tablespoon chopped fresh parsley

Cut off a 15-mm/½-inch slice from the top of each onion and a thin slice from the bottom. Remove the central part of the onions leaving a 15-mm/½-inch shell. Weigh 75 g/3 oz of the central parts and chop finely. (Use the remainder in another dish.)

Place onion shells in a large pan, cover with water and add a little salt. Bring to the boil, cover, lower the heat and simmer for 5 minutes and then remove the onions with a

dutch hotpot

4 hours

520 kcal/2184 kJ per portion

Beef brisket could also be used for this recipe although it is not as lean as topside.

Serves 6

1 kg/2¼ lbs topside of beef
1 teaspoon salt
1 bay leaf
1 kg/2¼ lbs carrots, diced
1 kg/2¼ lbs potatoes, peeled and quartered
1 kg/2¼ lbs onions, coarsely chopped
freshly ground black pepper

Bring 1 litre/1¾ pints of water to the boil in a deep pot or heavy casserole. Add the salt, meat, and bring the liquid back to the boil. Let it boil vigorously and skim off the scum that rises to the top. Add the bay leaf, partially cover the pan and lower the heat. Simmer the meat for 2½-3 hours or until

tender; add more water as necessary in the latter stages of cooking to keep the meat covered.

Add the carrots to the pot and simmer for 30 minutes. Then add the potatoes and onions. Simmer the mixture, uncovered, until the liquid has nearly evaporated, about 20 minutes.

Remove the meat from the pot and keep it warm. Remove and discard the bay leaf. Stir the contents of the pot, mashing the vegetables into a purée. Add a generous helping of pepper and a little more salt if necessary. Arrange the purée in the centre of a large warmed serving dish. Slice the meat thinly and place it around the purée. Serve at once, piping hot.

Serve with: Dijon mustard and dill pickles.

oxtail soup

4 hours + 2 hours soaking

110 kcal/462 kJ per portion (6 servings)

A rich beefy soup suitable for a dinner party or a family meal. Home-made soups will contain less salt than commercial varieties if you are discriminating as you season.

Serves 4-6

1 oxtail (or the small end pieces from 2 oxtails), skinned, jointed, trimmed and soaked for 2 hours
1 tablespoon flour
1 tablespoon oil
1 bacon knuckle, trimmed of fat
2 medium-sized carrots, finely chopped
2 medium-sized onions, finely chopped
2 small turnips, finely chopped
5 celery stalks, finely chopped
2 bay leaves
3 sprigs of parsley
1 teaspoon dried thyme
½ teaspoon dried marjoram
½ teaspoon dried tarragon
1 teaspoon tomato purée
salt and freshly ground black pepper
½ teaspoon cayenne pepper
2 tablespoons port, Madeira, Marsala or medium-dry sherry (optional)

oxtail soup

Pat the oxtail joints dry with absorbent paper and sprinkle them with flour. Heat the oil in a large, heavy-based saucepan over a moderate heat, then add the oxtail joints and brown them on all sides.

Add the bacon knuckle, vegetables, herbs and black pepper. Cook, covered, over a very low heat for 10-15 minutes, then pour in cold water to cover. Bring to the boil over a high heat, skim off any scum that rises to the top, then lower the heat. Simmer very gently for 3½ hours.

Remove the bacon knuckle and discard. Take out the pieces of oxtail and separate the meat from the bones. Remove any fat from the surface of the stock, then liquidize the stock and vegetables to a purée. Return to the pan with the meat.

Stir in the tomato purée and cayenne pepper and season to taste with salt and black pepper. Stir in the port, Madeira, Marsala or sherry, if using, stir and serve at once.

Serve with: warm fingers of toasted wholemeal bread.

pork chops in cider

| 1 hour | 385 kcal/1617 kJ per portion |

A classical combination of flavours in a very simple recipe.

Serves 4

4 pork chump chops
1 tablespoon oil
1 medium-sized onion, finely chopped
1 clove garlic, crushed
300 ml/½ pint sweet cider
2 sprigs rosemary
2 dessert apples, cored but not peeled
1 tablespoon cornflour
salt and freshly ground black pepper

Heat the oven to 180C/350F/Gas 4. Trim most of the fat from the chops and place under a moderate grill. Cook until browned on both sides. Meanwhile, heat the oil in a flameproof casserole, add the onion and garlic and cook over a moderate heat until the onion is lightly coloured.
Add the chops to the casserole followed by the cider. Add one sprig of rosemary and bring the mixture to the boil. Cover and cook in the oven for 30 minutes.
Slice the apples into rings, add to the casserole and stir to coat them with sauce. Cook for a further 10 minutes. Remove and discard the rosemary. In a small bowl, mix together the cornflour and a little of the sauce to make a smooth paste.
Using a slotted spoon, transfer the chops and apples to a heated serving dish and keep warm. Stir the cornflour paste into the sauce in the casserole and whisk over a high heat until the sauce boils and thickens. Taste and season if necessary, then pour the sauce over the chops and garnish with the remaining sprig of rosemary.

Serve with: Mashed potatoes and peas to increase the fibre content of the meal.

pork chops in cider

pork and chick-pea stew

2¼ hours
+ marinating
and cooking
the chick-peas

425 kcal/1785 kJ per portion

Chick-peas can be cooked in a pressure-cooker in 40 minutes.

Serves 4

800 g /1¾ lbs lean shoulder of pork, trimmed
   and cut into 2.5-cm /1-inch cubes
1 tablespoon oil
2 medium-sized onions, halved and thinly
   sliced
100 ml /3½ fl oz red wine
3 medium-sized tomatoes, blanched, skinned,
   seeded and chopped
1 bay leaf
1 large red pepper, sliced
100 g /4 oz dried chick-peas, soaked overnight
   and boiled for 1½-2 hours until tender
salt and pepper
freshly chopped parsley, to garnish

For the marinade:
1½ teaspoons salt
freshly ground black pepper
large pinch ground allspice
¼ teaspoon dried marjoram
2 large cloves garlic, crushed

Place the cubed pork in a bowl with the marinade ingredients and mix well. Cover and refrigerate for 8 hours or overnight, stirring once or twice (if convenient). Drain the meat and dry on absorbent paper; reserve the juice.
Heat the oil in a large frying-pan over a moderate heat. Add the pork, in batches if necessary, and fry, stirring, until it begins to brown. Transfer to a flameproof casserole, using a slotted spoon.
Add the onions to the frying pan and cook for a few minutes until softened, then add them to the casserole. Deglaze the frying-pan with the wine, stirring well so as to mix in the crusty bits from the bottom of the pan. Pour this into the casserole and add the tomatoes, bay leaf and reserved meat juices. Bring to simmering point, then lower the heat, cover and cook very gently for 30

minutes, stirring occasionally.
Add the sliced pepper and the chick-peas. Continue to cook, stirring occasionally, for a further 1-1½ hours until the meat is very tender.
Transfer the meat and vegetables to a heated serving dish using a slotted spoon. Boil the remaining juices quickly until they reduce and thicken slightly. Taste and adjust the seasoning, then pour over the pork. Sprinkle with parsley and serve.

Serve with: Broccoli or other dark green vegetable in season.

spiced leg of pork

3½ hours
+ 8 days
marinating

465 kcal/1953 kJ per portion

A useful dish when cooking for a crowd or for a buffet. Discarding the fat (which is easiest to do when the meat is cold) will reduce the calorie and fat intake.

Serves 14

2.5 kg /5 lbs leg of pork
2 celery stalks, washed and sliced
1 medium-sized onion, skinned and stuck with
   2 cloves
a twist of thinly pared lemon rind
1 tablespoon Muscovado sugar
dried breadcrumbs (optional)

For the preserving mixture:
50 g /2 oz coarse salt (sea salt)
50 g /2 oz fine salt (common kitchen salt)
2 teaspoons saltpetre or potassium nitrate
1 teaspoon black peppercorns
1 tablespoon coriander seeds
5-cm /2-inch piece cinnamon stick
2 teaspoons crumbled dried rosemary
½ teaspoon dried thyme
175 g /6 oz Muscovado sugar

Prepare the preserving mixture: using a pestle and mortar, crush all the ingredients, except the sugar, to a fine powder. Stir in sugar. Prick the pork all over with a small sterilized skewer or large darning needle and place it in a dry scalded dish; it should be a tight fit. Rub the preserving mixture thoroughly into the meat, particularly around the bone at both

ends. Cover the dish with foil and put it in the refrigerator. Rub the meat thoroughly with the salt mixture once each day for the next 7 days.
Rinse the meat in cold water, discard the preservatives and scrape off any salt. Place the pork in a large pan and add the celery, onion and cloves, lemon rind and sugar. Pour in enough water to cover and bring slowly to the boil. Cover the pan, lower the heat and simmer very gently for about 3 hours, until the pork is cooked – the juices should run clear when the meat is pierced with a sharp knife.
To serve hot, lift the pork from the pan and strip off the rind. Strain the cooking liquid and pour some of it into a heated serving jug to be used as a sauce.
To serve the meat cold, cool it in the liquid and then strip off the rinded fat. If you like, press about 6 tablespoons dried breadcrumbs into the fat on the top of the meat. Serve thinly sliced.

Serve with: Baked potatoes and a green salad.

stir-fried lamb and leeks

20 minutes

2

320 kcal /1344 kJ per portion

A very quick and economical dish to make. It can be made in a wok if you have one, although a frying-pan is perfectly satisfactory.

Serves 4

450 g /1 lb leg of lamb (weighed without the bone)
4-5 young leeks
1 clove garlic
2.5-cm /1-inch piece fresh root ginger, cut lengthways in 3-4 slices
1 teaspoon salt
3 tablespoons oil
2 tablespoons soy sauce
3 tablespoons Chinese yellow wine or dry sherry
freshly ground black pepper

Cut the lamb into 2 x 4-cm/¾ x 1½-inch strips. Wash the leeks thoroughly and cut into 2.5-cm/1-inch sections. Cut the garlic into thin slices and the ginger into short matchsticks. Rub the lamb with salt.
Heat the oil in a frying-pan or wok. When hot, add the lamb, garlic, and ginger. Stir 2-3 times and add the leeks. Continue stirring over high heat for 2-3 minutes. Sprinkle with soy sauce, wine and pepper and serve immediately in a warmed serving dish.

Serve with: Boiled brown rice.

lamb in red wine

lamb with yoghurt and paprika sauce

2¼ hours

370 kcal/1554 kJ per portion

To stabilize yoghurt, heat it with a small teaspoon of cornflour; this prevents the yoghurt from separating out when added to the casserole.

Serves 4

700 g /1½ lbs lean lamb, in 2.5-cm /1 inch cubes
salt and freshly ground black pepper
2 teaspoons mild paprika
1½ tablespoons oil
1 medium-sized onion, sliced
1 medium-sized red pepper, thinly sliced
400 g /14 oz canned tomatoes
1 tablespoon tomato purée
1 bay leaf
½ teaspoon dried oregano
150 ml /5 fl oz stabilized natural yoghurt
1 tablespoon chopped parsley, to garnish

Put the meat into a polythene bag with some salt and pepper and the paprika and shake until the meat is well coated.
Heat the oil in a frying-pan over a high heat, add the cubes of meat and fry them for about 5 minutes, turning them frequently so that they are sealed on all sides. Using a slotted spoon, transfer the meat to an ovenproof casserole.
Heat the oven to 180C/350F/Gas 4. Add the onion and red pepper to the fat remaining in the pan and stir. Fry over moderate heat for about 3 minutes, but do not allow the onion to brown. Add the tomatoes with their juice, the tomato purée, the bay leaf and oregano. Bring the sauce to a boil, season with salt and pepper and pour over the meat in the casserole. Stir to blend.
Cover the casserole and cook for 1½-1¾ hours, or until the meat is tender. Remove the casserole from the oven. Discard the bay leaf and stir in the yoghurt until the sauce is smooth and the colour is evenly distributed. Return the casserole to the oven for about 5 minutes to heat through. Sprinkle with the chopped parsley and serve hot.

Serve with: Sliced layered potatoes, oven-baked in milk and steamed carrots.

lamb in red wine

55 minute: + 3 hours marinating

310 kcal/1302 kJ per portion

This dish can be made using any type of red wine

Serves 4

700 g /1½ lbs lamb fillet
225 ml /8 fl oz red wine
2 tablespoons tomato purée
1 large clove garlic, crushed (optional)
2 sprigs rosemary
salt and freshly ground black pepper
75 ml /3 fl oz water

Put the wine in a bowl with the tomato purée, garlic, if using, rosemary and some salt and pepper. Stir well to mix.
Place the lamb fillet in a shallow flameproof dish and pour over the wine mixture. Cover and leave to marinate for at least 3 hours.
Heat the oven to 180C/350F/Gas 4.
Cover the dish with a lid or foil and cook the lamb in the oven for 30 minutes. Remove the cover and cook for a further 10 minutes. Transfer the lamb to a plate and keep hot in the lowest possible oven.
Carefully strain off any fat from the dish, then stir in the water. Place on top of the cooker and stir over moderate heat, scraping the sediment from the bottom of the dish with a wooden spoon. Bring to the boil, stirring constantly. Taste and adjust seasoning. Remove from heat and keep hot.
Slice the lamb into 2-cm/¾-inch thick round slices. Put them onto a warmed serving dish and spoon some of the sauce over the top. Pour the rest of the sauce into a warmed jug and hand separately.

Serve with: Seasonal green vegetables for a low-calorie meal.

watercress veal

1¼ hours | 310 kcal/1302 kJ per portion

A nouvelle cuisine style dish which should be served on individual plates for maximum visual effect.

Serves 4

50 g/2 oz shelled, halved walnuts
1 bunch of watercress, washed
25 g/1 oz butter
1 small onion, finely chopped
150 ml/5 fl oz soured cream
salt and freshly ground black pepper
lemon juice
milk (see recipe)
4 veal escalopes, thinly beaten out

Put the halved walnuts into a small bowl and pour over enough boiling water to cover. Leave to stand for 10 minutes. Discard the stalks from the watercress and chop the leaves.
Remove the walnuts from the water with a slotted spoon, and peel off the thin brown skins. Chop the nuts finely.
Melt half of the butter in a heavy-based frying-pan. When the foaming subsides, add the finely chopped onion and fry, stirring occasionally, over a moderate heat for about 5 minutes or until soft. Add the chopped watercress leaves, soured cream and chopped walnuts. Season with salt, freshly ground black pepper and lemon juice to taste. Cover the pan tightly and simmer gently over a low heat for 7-10 minutes (add a little milk if the sauce reduces and thickens too rapidly).
Remove the sauce from the heat and liquidize to a smooth purée. Return the sauce to a pan and keep warm over a very low heat, stirring occasionally.

Meanwhile, melt the remaining butter in a frying-pan. Cut each beaten escalope into 2 evenly-shaped, smaller slices. Sauté these over a medium heat until cooked through, turning once – about 3-4 minutes.
Arrange the veal on individual heated plates and spoon the sauce over the top.

Serve with: Tiny new potatoes and florets of broccoli.

liver-stuffed tomatoes

35 minutes

2

170 kcal /714 kJ per portion

These could be used as starters for a dinner-party or served as a light lunch or supper dish.

Serves 4

100 g /4 oz chicken livers, finely chopped
8 firm tomatoes
2 bacon rashers, rind removed and finely chopped
1 small onion, finely chopped
100 g /4 oz mushrooms, finely chopped
salt and freshly ground black pepper
75 g /3 oz fresh soft wholemeal breadcrumbs
1 teaspoon dried thyme
1 tablespoon finely chopped fresh parsley
1 tablespoon oil plus a little extra for greasing baking sheet
parsley sprigs, to garnish

Heat the oven to 180C/350F/Gas 4 and lightly oil a baking sheet.
Cut the tops off the tomatoes and set aside. Carefully scoop out the insides of the tomatoes (the pulp can be added to a soup or stew), taking care not to pierce the skins.
Gently cook the bacon in a frying pan until the fat runs out. Add the onion and fry for 5-6 minutes until the bacon and onion are cooked but not coloured. Add the mushrooms and cook for a further minute, then add the chicken livers and cook for about 5 minutes until well browned, stirring all the time. Season with salt and pepper to taste and stir in the breadcrumbs, thyme and parsley.
Divide the filling evenly between the tomatoes. Replace the lids and place the tomatoes on the baking sheet. Brush them with a little oil and bake in the oven for 15 minutes.
Using a large spoon, transfer the tomatoes to a warmed serving dish and serve hot, garnished with parsley sprigs.

Serve with: Warm wholemeal rolls and a green salad.

stir-fried liver

stir-fried liver

30 minutes

2

270 kcal /1134 kJ per portion

As with all dishes containing liver, this one is a very good source of iron. It is also economical.

Serves 4

450 g /1 lb pig's liver, in one piece
1 tablespoon cornflour
1 teaspoon salt
1 teaspoon ground ginger
2 tablespoons water
1 tablespoon medium-dry sherry
2 tablespoons plus 1 teaspoon oil
1 large clove garlic, crushed
1½ tablespoons coarsely chopped spring onion tops

For the sauce:
1½ tablespoons soy sauce
1 tablespoon medium sherry
1 tablespoon tomato purée
1½ tablespoons wine vinegar
1½ tablespoons chicken stock
1 teaspoon sugar.

Wash the liver under cold running water and pat dry with absorbent paper. Trim away all traces of thin outer skin or veins. With a sharp knife cut into 3-mm/⅛-inch thick slices and then into 2.5-cm/1-inch strips.
In a bowl, combine the cornflour, salt and ginger. Blend in 2 tablespoons water, the sherry and 1 teaspoon oil.
Add the liver slices and gently turn so as to coat them with the cornflour mixture. Leave to stand for 15 minutes.
In a mixing bowl, combine all the sauce ingredients until well blended.
Heat the remaining oil in a frying-pan over moderate heat. When sizzling, add the liver, spreading the pieces evenly over the pan.
Raise the heat and cook the liver briskly, stirring, for 30 seconds.
Sprinkle in the garlic and spring onions and continue stir-frying for another 30 seconds. Pour the sauce mixture into the pan, bring to the boil and cook, stirring constantly, for a further 30 seconds. Serve immediately.

Serve with: Boiled brown rice and a bean sprout salad.

vietnamese chicken with lemon balm

30 minutes + 20 minutes marinating

160 kcal /672 kJ per portion

A delicately seasoned rather than heavily spiced dish. If you cannot obtain lemon balm, substitute French tarragon.

Serves 4

4 dried mushrooms
2 tablespoons dry sherry
2 teaspoons soy sauce
1 teaspoon grated fresh ginger
salt and freshly ground black pepper
225 g /8 oz boneless chicken breast, thinly
   sliced
2 tablespoons oil
100 g /4 oz drained, canned bamboo shoots,
   thinly sliced
225 g /8 oz Chinese cabbage, shredded
2 tablespoons chopped fresh lemon balm or
   French tarragon
2 teaspoons cornflour
2 tablespoons water

Soak the mushrooms in warm water to cover for 20 minutes. Mix together the sherry, soy sauce, ginger, ¼ teaspoon salt and a generous grinding of pepper. Pour over the chicken and allow to marinate for 20 minutes, turning the chicken slices occasionally.
Drain and thinly slice the mushrooms. Heat the oil in a large thin frying-pan or wok over medium-high heat and stir-fry the mushrooms, bamboo shoots and Chinese cabbage for 1 minute.
Push the vegetables to the sides of the pan. Put the chicken with the marinade and the lemon balm into the centre of the pan and stir-fry for 4 minutes.
Blend the cornflour with the water, add it to the pan and stir all the ingredients together. Continue cooking and stirring until the sauce thickens and clears – about 1 minute. Taste and adjust the seasoning if necessary. Serve immediately.

Serve with: Boiled brown rice.

rabbit and artichoke fricassée

2¼ hours

345 kcal /1449 kJ per portion

Any type of stock would be suitable for this dish although, if it is very strong, it would be better to dilute it so that the taste of the rabbit will not be masked. In summer, a 15-cm /6-in length of cucumber could be substituted for the Jerusalem artichokes.

Serves 4

1 young rabbit, jointed, or 4 large leg portions
1 medium-sized onion, chopped
100 g /4 oz turnip, diced
100 g /4 oz celery heart, chopped
1 bouquet garni
salt and freshly ground white pepper
700 ml /1¼ pint pale coloured stock
350 g /12 oz Jerusalem artichokes, peeled, and
   larger ones halved
300 ml /½ pint milk
6 tablespoons fresh wholemeal breadcrumbs
2 tablespoons cornflour
¼ teaspoon dry mustard

Put the rabbit portions into a large saucepan with the onion, turnip and celery, bouquet garni and a little seasoning. Pour in the stock and bring to the boil. Stir once, skim the surface thoroughly, lower the heat and cover. Simmer the mixture for 1 hour.
Add the artichokes and milk to the pan, bring the mixture back to the simmering point, cover and cook for a further 30 minutes, or until the rabbit is tender. Remove the bouquet garni.
Heat the grill to a medium heat and place the breadcrumbs in a shallow tin or grill pan under the grill. Toast them, turning frequently, until the crumbs are crisp.
Spoon out a few tablespoons of the liquid from the saucepan and combine with the cornflour and mustard until smooth. Pour into a separate saucepan and place over moderate heat. Strain the stock from the fricassée and add it gradually to the cornflour mixture, stirring constantly. When all the liquid has been added, bring to the boil, still stirring. Lower the heat and simmer gently for 3 minutes. Adjust the seasoning. Pour the

sauce over the rabbit and vegetables and stir. Serve the fricassée in a warm tureen or deep platter, sprinkled with the toasted crumbs.

Serve with: Grilled tomatoes and a dark green vegetable.

cock-a-leekie

1½ hours + soaking prunes

140 kcal /588 kJ per portion (soup only)

A traditional Scottish dish which is both a substantial soup and a main course.

Serves 6

1.8 kg /4 lbs oven-ready chicken, plus the
   giblets
salt and freshly ground black pepper
1.1 litre /2 pints cold water
1 large onion, chopped
1 chicken stock cube
450 g /1 lb leeks, trimmed and washed
100 g /4 oz prunes, soaked overnight and
   stoned
2 tablespoons long-grain rice
2 tablespoons finely chopped parsley

Wash the chicken and season it inside and out. Put into a deep saucepan with the giblets (except the liver) and the water. Bring slowly to the boil, skimming off any scum as it rises.
Add the onion and crumbled stock cube, cover tightly, reduce heat and simmer very gently for 1 hour.
Meanwhile cut the leeks in thin diagonal slices. At the end of the hour, add them to the pot, with the prunes and rice. Continue simmering for 20 minutes, then test the chicken to see if it is cooked: the juices should run clear when the drumstick is pierced with a skewer.
Lift out the chicken and giblets. Spoon off the fat on the top of the broth.
Shred 200 g /7 oz of the cooked chicken and add to the broth. Correct the seasoning and serve, sprinkled with parsley.

Serve with: Granary bread or rolls. The remainder of the chicken could be served cold with a salad.

cock-a-leekie

poached chicken breasts with cucumber sauce

turkey and asparagus apollo

20 minutes

250 kcal/1050 kJ per portion

Serves 4

350 g/12 oz canned asparagus spears
350 ml/12 fl oz chicken stock
40 g/1½ oz wholemeal flour
150 ml/5 fl oz natural yoghurt
1 egg, beaten
2 teaspoons lemon juice
salt and freshly ground black pepper
350 g/12 oz cooked turkey meat
2 hard-boiled eggs

Drain the liquid from the asparagus and make it up to 425 ml/15 fl oz with chicken stock. Reserve some of the best spears for garnishing and chop the rest into 2.5-cm/1-inch lengths.

Combine the flour, yoghurt and egg in a saucepan and gradually stir in the measured liquid. Bring almost to the boil, stirring all the time, then lower the heat and cook, without boiling for 5 minutes. Stir in the lemon juice and season to taste.

Cut the turkey into bite-sized pieces and add to the sauce, letting them heat through. Coarsely chop one of the eggs and stir into the sauce with the asparagus pieces. Heat through and check seasoning.

Turn the mixture into a heated serving dish and garnish with the other egg, thinly sliced, and the reserved asparagus spears.

Serve with: Lightly buttered triangles of hot toast.

poached chicken breasts with cucumber sauce

45 minutes

280 kcal/1176 kJ per portion

Add a few drops of green food colouring to the sauce to tinge it an appetising pale green colour.

Serves 4

1 medium-sized cucumber, peeled
425 ml/15 fl oz chicken stock
150 ml/5 fl oz dry white wine
½ small onion, finely chopped
6 black peppercorns
1 bay leaf
salt
4 chicken breasts, skinned and boned
25 g/1 oz butter
40 g/1½ oz flour
150 ml/5 fl oz milk
150 ml/5 fl oz natural yoghurt
grated nutmeg
cucumber slices, to garnish

Bring a saucepan of water to the boil. Roughly chop the cucumber and place the pieces to steam, covered, in a sieve, set over the boiling water. When the cucumber is just soft (about 10 minutes) liquidize or press through a sieve to form a purée.
Bring the chicken stock and wine to the boil in a large saucepan. Add the onion, peppercorns, bay leaf and salt to taste. Add the chicken breasts, cover the pan, lower the heat and simmer gently for about 15 minutes, until the chicken is tender.
Meanwhile, prepare the sauce: melt the butter in a saucepan and stir in the flour. Cook for 1-2 minutes then take the pan off the heat and gradually add the milk, then the yoghurt, stirring constantly.
Return the pan to the heat, stir in 1-2 tablespoons liquor from the simmering chicken breasts and beat well to make a smooth sauce. Season to taste with salt and nutmeg.
Add the cucumber purée and simmer gently for a few more minutes. Lift the chicken breasts from the poaching liquor with a slotted spoon and arrange them on a warm serving dish. Pour the sauce over the chicken, and garnish with cucumber slices.

Serve with: Saffron rice, made by adding a few strands of saffron to the water when boiling the rice, and a green salad.

stir-fried chicken and prawns

20 minutes

235 kcal/987 kJ per portion

Stir-frying is a quick and generally healthy way to cook meat, fish and vegetables. Hoisin sauce is available at Chinese supermarkets; it is a sweet barbecue sauce.

Serves 4

225 g/8 oz chicken breasts, cut in small cubes
225 g/8 oz shelled prawns, defrosted if frozen
salt
2 tablespoons oil
100 g/4 oz button mushrooms, wiped
2 spring onions, sliced
10-cm/4-inch piece of cucumber, cubed
15 g/½ oz lard
4 teaspoons soy paste
2 teaspoons soy sauce
2 teaspoons tomato puree
2 teaspoons hoisin sauce
1 tablespoon sherry
1 teaspoon chilli sauce

Sprinkle the prawns with salt and set on one side while you prepare the chicken and vegetables.
Heat the oil in a frying-pan over a high heat and cook the mushrooms for 1 minute. Add the chicken and prawns, stir for 30 seconds, then add the spring onions and cucumber. Stir over a high heat for 1½ minutes, then transfer to a plate.
Add the lard to the pan and when melted add all the remaining ingredients. Stir them over a high heat and, when blended and bubbling, tip the chicken mixture back into the pan. Stir for 1 minute and serve at once.

Serve with: Boiled rice or noodles.

turkey in honey and ginger

turkey in honey and ginger

1¼ hours

310 kcal/1302 kJ per portion

A low-fat dish with plenty of flavour, it could, of course, be made using chicken instead.

Serves 4

4 turkey breast portions, skinned
1 tablespoon oil
100 ml/3½ fl oz clear honey
2 tablespoons Dijon mustard
1 teaspoon ground ginger
salt and freshly ground black pepper
watercress to garnish

Heat the oven to 180C/350F/Gas 4.
Heat the oil in a flameproof casserole just large enough to take the turkey portions in a single layer. Stir the honey, mustard and ginger into the oil. When smooth remove from the heat and season to taste with salt and pepper.
Place the turkey pieces in the casserole, turning them to coat thoroughly with the sauce.
Bake for 30 minutes, basting occasionally. Turn the turkey portions and cook for 30 minutes more, basting, until tender. Garnish with watercress.

Serve with: Steamed rice.

salmon salad in lemon shells

30 minutes

65 kcal/273 kJ per portion

Look for mooli in large greengrocers. It is a large white root — a type of radish, and is particularly complementary to the other flavours in this dish.

Serves 4

2 large unblemished lemons
100 g /4 oz mooli or small white turnip
100 g /4 oz young carrots
100 g /4 oz canned salmon
2 teaspoons sugar
salt
chopped spring onions, to garnish

Halve the lemons and squeeze out the juice. Cut around the remaining flesh just inside the skins and scoop it out to leave 4 empty half shells.
Scrub and grate the mooli and carrots. Drain and shred the salmon. In a bowl combine the mooli, salmon, sugar and a little salt. Stir in 1 tablespoon lemon juice.

Pile the salmon salad into the lemon shells and place on individual serving plates. Garnish with chopped spring onion and sprinkle with a little lemon juice just before serving.

Serve with: Thinly sliced wholemeal bread.

salmon salad in lemon shells

jellied tomato and prawn ring

55 minutes
+1 hour
chilling

190 kcal/798 kJ per
portion (4 servings)

This would be ideal as part of a cold buffet or as an attractive starter to a meal.

Serves 4 (or 8 as a starter)

750 g/1½ lbs ripe tomatoes
juice of ½ lemon
1 medium-sized onion, finely chopped
1 clove garlic, finely chopped
2 teaspoons paprika pepper
pinch of cayenne pepper
4 basil leaves or 1 teaspoon dried basil
200 ml/7 fl oz dry white wine
25 g/1 oz powdered gelatine
oil for greasing
350 g/12 oz peeled cooked prawns
3 tablespoons chopped parsley

For the tomato salad:
3 large, firm tomatoes
1 tablespoon oil
1 tablespoon lemon juice
2 teaspoons tomato purée
½ teaspoon paprika pepper
2 drops Tabasco
sprigs of watercress or mustard and cress

Chop the ripe tomatoes and put them into a saucepan with the lemon juice, onion, garlic, paprika and cayenne peppers, basic and all but 4 tablespoons of the wine. Cover and cook very gently on a low heat for 20 minutes, until the tomatoes are reduced to a purée. Meanwhile sprinkle the gelatine over the rest of the wine in a small bowl.
Rub the tomato mixture through a sieve. Return the purée to the rinsed pan, set it on a low heat and stir in the soaked gelatine; continue to stir until it has dissolved.
Remove the pan from the heat. Lightly oil a 22-cm/9-inch ring mould, then pour in the tomato mixture to a depth of 15 mm/½ inch. Put into the refrigerator for about 15 minutes, or until set.
Sprinkle half the parsley over the set tomato jelly. Cover with the prawns in an even layer and sprinkle over the rest of the parsley. Pour in the remaining tomato jelly and put the ring

into the refrigerator for at least 1 hour, to set. To make the salad, chop the firm tomatoes fairly coarsely and put them in a bowl. Beat together the oil, lemon juice, tomato purée, paprika pepper and Tabasco, and gently toss this dressing into the tomatoes.
Wring out a tea towel in hot water and hold it around the mould for a few seconds. Centre a large flat serving plate upside down on top of the mould and invert the mould and plate. Holding the mould and plate firmly with both hands, give one or two firm shakes to release the jelly from the mould. Fill the centre with the tomato salad and garnish with watercress or mustard and cress.

Serve with: Crusty granary bread.

prawn bisque

50 minutes
(6 servings)

85 kcal/357 kJ per
portion (6 servings)

Most supermarkets sell set or thickened yoghurt; it puts the finishing touch to this delicious soup.

Serves 4-6

350 g/12 oz cooked unshelled prawns
250 g/10 oz raw fish trimmings
1 medium-sized onion, sliced
1 tablespoon tomato purée
1 bay leaf
3 thin strips lemon zest
900 ml/1½ pints water
25 g/1 oz butter
25 g/1 oz flour
salt and freshly ground black pepper
pinch of grated nutmeg
2 teaspoons lemon juice
4 tablespoons set yoghurt, to serve

Peel the prawns. Put the heads and shells into a large saucepan with the fish trimmings, onion, tomato purée, bay leaf and lemon zest. Add the water, bring to the boil, then lower the heat and simmer very gently for about 20 minutes.
Strain the contents of the pan into a bowl through a nylon sieve and discard the debris left in the sieve.
Melt the butter in the rinsed-out pan. Add

prawn bisque

the flour and cook, stirring gently, for 2 minutes. Gradually blend in the strained fish stock, stirring continuously. When all the stock has been added, allow the soup to simmer for 4-5 minutes, taste and season with salt, pepper, nutmeg and lemon juice. Add the peeled prawns to the soup and continue to simmer for a few minutes for the prawns to warm through.
Pour the soup into a warmed tureen or serving dish and swirl in the yoghurt. Serve immediately.

Serve with: Melba toast or oatcakes.

cold seafood platter

cold seafood platter

45 minutes + cooling

145 kcal /609 kJ per portion

Serves 4

450 g /1 lb mussels, scrubbed and bearded
150 ml /5 fl oz water
150 ml /5 fl oz dry white wine
8 raw scampi, with heads and shells on
8 large scallops

For the sauce:
1 tablespoon oil
1 onion, finely chopped
1 clove garlic, crushed
1 green pepper, finely diced
450 g /1 lb tomatoes, blanched, skinned and chopped
2 teaspoons lemon juice
¼ teaspoon ground coriander
½ teaspoon paprika
½ teaspoon cumin
salt and freshly ground black pepper

First make the sauce: heat the oil in a saucepan and sauté the finely chopped onion until soft – about 5 minutes. Add the crushed garlic and the finely diced pepper and continue cooking, stirring occasionally, for 5 minutes. Add the tomatoes, lemon juice, coriander, paprika and cumin. Stir well and season with salt and freshly ground black pepper. Simmer the sauce gently for 20 minutes, stirring occasionally. Remove from the heat and cool.

Meanwhile, discard any mussels that have open shells and put the remainder in a large saucepan with the water and the wine. Cover the pan tightly and place over a high heat, shaking the pan occasionally, for about 5 minutes or until the mussels have opened. Strain the mussels, reserving the liquor, discard any that have not opened and leave the remainder aside to cool. When cold, remove the mussels from the shells and discard the shells.

Bring the reserved liquor to the boil, add the scampi and turn the heat down. Simmer for 1½-2 minutes. Remove the scampi with a slotted spoon and set aside to cool. Separate the orange corals from each scallop and remove and discard the black membrane. Poach the scallops for 3-5 minutes in the liquor, adding the corals for the last minute of the cooking time. Drain and leave to cool.

To arrange, pour the sauce into individual ramekins and place one on each serving plate. Arrange the scampi and mussels on the plates. Slice the scallops in half horizontally and arrange them with the corals placed decoratively on top. Serve accompanied by fingerbowls and large napkins.

cucumber and crabmeat salad

50 minutes + 1 hour chilling

115 kcal /483 kJ per portion

Either freshly cooked or tinned crabmeat could be used for this recipe.

Serves 4

1 medium-sized cucumber
salt
6 spring onions
350 g /12 oz crabmeat

For the dressing:
½ teaspoon salt
½ teaspoon freshly ground black pepper
2 teaspoons ground ginger
1 tablespoon soy sauce
1 tablespoon olive oil

Cut the cucumber into 4 lengthways, remove any seeds, then chop into 15-mm /½-inch chunks. Sprinkle with salt and let stand for 30 minutes.

Cut off and reserve the green stems from the spring onions. Finely slice the white part and mix with the drained cucumber. Arrange around the edge of 4 serving dishes. Pile the crabmeat in the centre of each dish, garnish with the green stalks, shredded, cover with cling film and chill in the refrigerator for at least 1 hour.

Combine the ingredients for the dressing mixing them thoroughly. Serve the salad with the dressing handed round separately.

Serve with: Potato salad.

mussel and potato salad

1¼ hours + preparing mussels + cooling

255 kcal /1071 kJ per portion

Serves 4

1 kg /2¼ lbs mussels in their shells, scrubbed and bearded
4 tablespoons dry white wine
2 shallots, chopped
a sprig of thyme
a few parsley stalks
salt and freshly ground black pepper
450 g /1 lb small new potatoes
1 tender celery stalk, thinly sliced
1 tablespoon olive oil
1 tablespoon lemon juice
2 tablespoons cooked peas

Discard any mussels that have open shells and put the remainder into a large saucepan with the wine, shallots, thyme, parsley and several grinds of pepper. Cover and cook over high heat for 5-6 minutes, shaking the pan frequently. Remove the mussels from the pan as they open. Reserve a few in their shells for garnishing and discard the remaining shells, together with any mussels that fail to open. Set the mussels aside to cool, and strain the cooking liquid through a muslin-lined strainer into a small pan.

Boil the potatoes in lightly salted water until just tender, then drain, skin and cut into 5-mm /¼-inch slices. Boil the mussel liquor briskly until well reduced, pour over the warm potatoes and then set aside until cold.

To serve, drain any surplus liquid from the potatoes and spread the potatoes and celery in a shallow serving dish. Arrange the mussels on top of the potatoes. Mix the oil and lemon juice together and spoon over the mussels.

Sprinkle the peas on top of the salad and surround it with the reserved mussels in their shells.

Serve with: Crusty bread and a green salad.

seafood salad

1 hour + cooling

340 kcal /1428 kJ per portion

Serves 4

700 g /1½ lbs or 1½ pts mussels in their shells, scrubbed and bearded
350 g /12 oz squid
350 g /12 oz large prawns in their shells
350 g /12 oz scallops
100 g /4 oz peeled, cooked shrimps
4 tablespoons olive oil
1 small onion
1 bay leaf
salt and freshly ground black pepper
1 tablespoon wine vinegar
4 tablespoons lemon juice
2 tablespoons capers
3 tablespoons chopped parsley
1 small clove garlic, finely chopped
chopped parsley, to garnish

Discard any mussels that have open shells and set the remainder aside.
To clean the squid, hold the sac in one hand and with the other, pull off the tentacles. As you pull them, the internal organs should come out of the sac. Cut off the head and discard it and the organs. Reserve the tentacles. Remove the bone from the sac and peel off the violet 'skin', holding the squid under running water. Wash the sac and tentacles thoroughly.
Place the mussels in a large saucepan with 1 tablespoon of the oil and 125 ml/4 fl oz of water. Cover the pan and cook over high heat until the mussels open, stirring occasionally. Lift them out of the pan as they open and discard any that do not open. Remove the mussels from the shells and place in a large serving dish.
Add 2 litres/3½ pints water, the onion, bay leaf and 1 teaspoon salt to the mussel liquid in the saucepan. Bring to the boil, add the squid, lower the heat and simmer, covered, for 10 minutes.
Wash the prawns in cold water and add them to the pan with the squid. Cook, covered, for a further 10 minutes. When the squid are tender, drain them with the prawns (reserve the liquid for making fish soup or sauce the

seafood salad

next day). Discard the onion and bay leaf. Rinse the scallops under cold water. Bring 1 litre/1¾ pint of water to the boil. Add the vinegar, 1 teaspoon salt and the scallops. Cook for 2-3 minutes, then drain.
Peel the prawns and cut them into 15-mm/½-inch sections. Cut the squid into 15-mm/½-inch strips and the scallops into slightly larger cubes. Add the prawns and scallops to the mussels with the peeled shrimps.
In a small bowl mix together the remaining oil, the lemon juice, capers, parsley, chopped garlic and plenty of black pepper. Taste and add salt if necessary. Pour the sauce over the seafood and toss gently but thoroughly. Allow the mixture to stand at room temperature for 2 hours before serving.
Just before serving, sprinkle the extra chopped parsley over the salad.

Serve with: Herb or garlic bread and a green salad.

aromatic fish parcels

45 minutes

180 kcal /760 kJ per portion

You could use haddock, cod, coley or whiting fillets instead of the perch in this recipe.

Serves 4

4 pike or perch fillets, weighing about 600 g /1¼ lbs in all
150 g /5 oz leeks, washed and sliced
4 medium-sized tomatoes, sliced
salt and freshly ground black pepper
25 g /1 oz butter
3 tablespoons mixed finely chopped dill and parsley
2 teaspoons finely chopped chives

Heat the oven to 200F/400C/Gas 6. Simmer the leeks in a little water until soft, then drain.
Divide the leeks into 4 equal portions and place each portion on a large piece of foil. Place a sliced tomato on top of each layer of leek and season with salt and pepper.
Cut the fish fillets in half lengthways and place them on a flat surface, skin side down. Sprinkle with salt and pepper.

Mix the butter with the herbs and spread the mixture over the fillets. Roll up each one and secure it with a cocktail stick.
Place two rolls on each portion of vegetables, in each parcel and fold the foil over them to make 4 well sealed parcels.
Put the parcels in a baking dish and bake in the oven for about 20 minutes. Serve at once.

Serve with: Boiled potatoes and peas.

tuna and bean salad

15 minutes + chilling

225 kcal /945 kJ per portion

Serves 4

200 g /7 oz can tuna in brine, drained
215 g /7½ oz can cannellini beans
215 g /7½ oz can red kidney beans
1 small onion, chopped
lemon twists, to garnish

For the dressing:
3 tablespoons olive oil
2 tablespoons lemon juice
1 tablespoon chopped fresh parsley
salt and freshly ground black pepper

Make the dressing: put the oil in screw-top jar with lemon juice, parsley and some salt and pepper. Cover and shake well.
Rinse the beans under cold running water, then drain them thoroughly and tip into a large bowl. Add the onion and dressing and toss well.
Using a fork, gently flake the tuna into salad. Stir gently to mix, cover and refrigerate until required.
To serve, gently stir the salad, then divide between 4 individual bowls. Garnish with lemon twists.

Serve with: Wholemeal bread.

cold fruity plaice

1 hour + cooling

300 kcal / 1260 kJ per portion

Serves 8

8 plaice fillets, all skin removed
juice of ½ lemon
3 oranges
salt and freshly ground black pepper
butter for greasing
25 g / 1 oz butter, cut in small pieces
75 ml / 3 fl oz natural yoghurt
75 ml / 3 fl oz low-calorie mayonnaise

To garnish:
paprika
50 g / 2 oz canned anchovy fillets, drained

Heat the oven to 180C/350F/Gas 4. Wash the plaice fillets and dry them well on absorbent paper. Sprinkle with the lemon juice and the juice of half an orange. Season with salt and pepper. Finely grate the rind of 1 orange over the fish and roll up the fillets, beginning at the head end. Secure them with wooden cocktail sticks and place in a buttered ovenproof dish.
Squeeze the juice of another half orange over the fish, dot with the butter, then cover the dish with buttered greaseproof paper or foil. Bake in the centre of the oven for about 20 minutes, or until the fillets are tender but still firm. Remove the dish from the oven and leave to cool.
Lift the cold fillets on to a shallow serving dish and remove the cocktail sticks.
Combine the yoghurt and the mayonnaise. Grate the rind and squeeze the juice of half an orange. Add the juice to the mayonnaise mixture, a drop at a time, and stir in the grated rind. Coat the fillets with this mixture and sprinkle lightly with paprika. Halve the anchovy fillets lengthways and arrange 2 halves over each little 'parcel' of fish.
Peel the remaining 1½ oranges, removing all the pith, and cut them into thin slices with a sharp serrated knife. Serve separately as an accompaniment.

Serve with: A new potato salad and a salad of watercress, cucumber and apple.

golden fish soufflé

1¼ hours

220 kcal / 924 kJ per portion

Serves 4

350 g / 12 oz smoked cod fillets, skinned
300 ml / ½ pint skimmed milk
2 tablespoons oil
25 g / 1 oz flour
1 medium-sized egg, separated
3 medium-sized egg whites
salt and freshly ground black pepper
25 g / 1 oz Edam cheese, grated

In a large saucepan, poach the fish in the skimmed milk for 15 minutes, until tender. Remove the fish with a slotted spoon and flake coarsely. Strain the milk into a jug and reserve.
Heat the oven to 190C/375F/Gas 5. Heat the oil in the rinsed-out saucepan, add the flour and cook, stirring for 1 minute. Remove from the heat and stir in the reserved cooking liquid.
Return the pan to the heat, bring to the boil and simmer gently for 2 minutes, stirring constantly.
Remove from the heat, cool for 5 minutes, then add the flaked fish and egg yolk. Whisk the egg whites until stiff and fold into the fish mixture. Season with salt and pepper. Spoon the mixture into a greased 1.1-litre/2-pint soufflé dish. Sprinkle with the grated cheese. Bake in the oven for 35-40 minutes until well risen and golden brown. Serve immediately.

Serve with: Green vegetables or a green salad.

finnish fish soup

40 minutes + making stock

320 kcal / 1344 kJ per portion

To make fish stock, boil up the trimmings from the fish e.g. head, skin, tail and bones with a chopped onion, chopped celery and some sprigs of parsley.

Serves 4

350-450 g / 12 oz-1 lb fish fillets such as salmon, trout, or perch. cut into small pieces
1 tablespoon oil
2 medium-sized onions, finely chopped
4-5 medium-sized potatoes
1.1 litres / 2 pints fish stock
10 allspice berries, crushed
100 ml / 3½ fl oz milk
salt
lemon juice (optional)
2 tablespoons chopped dill
1 tablespoon snipped chives

Heat the oil in a large saucepan over low heat. Add the onions and cook for 5 minutes, or until soft and transparent.
Meanwhile, peel the potatoes and cut them into small pieces. Add the fish stock, allspice berries and the potatoes to the pan. Bring to the boil, then lower the heat and simmer for about 10 minutes.
Add the pieces of fish to the soup and simmer gently for about 5 minutes or until the fish is cooked.
Add the milk. Bring back to the boil then remove from the heat. Season with salt and a little lemon juice, if you wish. Sprinkle with the chopped dill and chives and serve at once.

Serve with: Dark rye bread.

sea bass with orange sauce

sea bass with orange sauce

45 minutes

330 kcal /1386 kJ per portion

Serves 4

4 x 175 g /6 oz skinned and boned sea bass steaks, with skins and bones reserved
200 ml /7 fl oz water
1 bay leaf
salt and freshly ground black pepper
2 tablespoons olive oil
½ orange, cut into very thin slices

For the sauce:
1 tablespoon olive oil
50 g /2 oz flour
150 ml /5 fl oz freshly squeezed orange juice (2-3 oranges)
juice of ½ lemon
grated rind of 1 orange

Simmer the skin and bones of the sea bass in the water with the bay leaf for 20 minutes. Season, strain and reserve.
Heat the oil in a frying-pan over medium heat and fry the fish for about 5 minutes on each side until golden. Drain the steaks on absorbent paper, transfer them to a hot serving dish and keep warm.
To make the sauce, add the oil to the juices in the frying-pan and stir in the flour. Gradually add 150ml/5 fl oz of the reserved fish stock together with the orange and lemon juices, stirring all the time to keep the sauce smooth. Cook over low heat, stirring, until the sauce has thickened and is smooth. Stir in the orange rind, season to taste. Pour the sauce over the fish steaks and garnish with the orange slices.

Serve with: Watercress salad.

baked barramundi

baked barramundi

1¼ hours

220 kcal /924 kJ per portion

Barramundi is an Australian fish. Cod, haddock or hake can be used with equal success in this recipe.

Serves 6

*1.3-1.5 kg /3-3½ lbs whole white sea fish, such
    as barramundi, hake, haddock or cod
1 lemon
1 large green pepper
100 g /4 oz cooked brown rice
1 celery stalk, finely chopped
1 medium-sized onion, finely chopped
1 teaspoon finely chopped fresh sage leaves
salt and freshly ground black pepper
15 g /½ oz butter, melted
1 large tomato, sliced
15g /½ oz chilled butter, cut into flakes
1 tablespoon chopped parsley*

Remove the head and fins from the fish; clean and scale it if necessary. Rinse the fish under cold water, inside and out, and wipe it dry with absorbent paper.
Cut the lemon in half. Rub the fish inside and out with the cut side of one of the halves, then squeeze and reserve the juice, together with the other half. Cut the pepper in half, seed it and slice one half thinly and reserve. Chop the second half.
Heat the oven to 180C/350F/Gas 4. Mix the chopped pepper, rice, celery, chopped onion and sage together in a bowl. Mix in some or all of the reserved lemon juice, to taste, and season well with salt and pepper. Stuff the fish with the mixture. Grease a baking dish which will hold the fish comfortably. Put in the fish and brush it with the melted butter. Arrange the pepper and tomato slices alternately in a line on top of the fish. Dot with the chilled butter.
Bake the fish for 35-40 minutes, basting with butter occasionally. Cut the reserved lemon half into small wedges.
Serve the fish garnished with chopped parsley and lemon wedges.

Serve with: Lightly cooked green beans and baked potatoes.

haddock with sorrel

55 minutes   180 kcal /756 kJ per portion

Serves 4

700 g /1½ lbs haddock fillets
300 ml /½ pint water
100 ml /3½ fl oz dry white wine
1 medium-sized onion, thinly sliced
1 medium-sized carrot, thinly sliced
1 celery stalk, chopped
1 bouquet garni
1 teaspoon black peppercorns
50 g /2 oz sorrel leaves, chopped
100 g /4 oz fromage blanc, Quark or curd
    cheese
celery leaves, to garnish

Skin the haddock fillets, reserving the skin.
Cut the fish into small serving pieces.
Put the skin into a saucepan with the water,
the wine, onion, carrot and celery, bouquet
garni and peppercorns. Bring to the boil,
then boil gently, uncovered, for about 20
minutes or until the liquid is reduced by half.
Strain the liquid into a large saucepan and
bring it just to boiling point. Add the
haddock pieces and poach for about 3
minutes, or until cooked through but still
firm. Lift them onto a warmed serving dish
with a slotted spoon and keep warm.
Add the sorrel to the simmering liquid and
cook for 1 minute, then transfer the sorrel
and the liquid to a blender or food processor.
Add the fromage blanc, Quark or curd
cheese and process until smooth.
Reheat the sauce very gently without boiling,
then spoon over the haddock, garnish with
the celery leaves and serve.

Serve with: Boiled potatoes or brown rice
and grilled tomatoes.

trawler stew

trawler stew

1 hour portion   300 kcal /1260 kJ per

Serves 4

1 tablespoon oil
1 large onion, sliced
2 cloves garlic, crushed
1 medium-sized green pepper, seeded and
    sliced
400 g /14 oz canned tomatoes
300 ml /1½ pint cider
salt and freshly ground black pepper
pinch of cayenne
450 g /1 lb potatoes, peeled and diced
700 g /1½ lbs white fish, skinned and cut into
    7.5-cm /3-inch slices
2 tablespoons chopped parsley

Heat the oil in a flameproof casserole or a pan
and fry the onion and garlic over low heat,
stirring once or twice, for 4-5 minutes. Add
the green pepper, stir, then add the tomatoes
with their juice and the cider. Season with
salt, pepper and cayenne. Bring to the boil,
lower the heat and simmer, uncovered, for 15
minutes.
Stir in the potatoes, cover and cook for a
further 20 minutes. Add the slices of fish and
parsley. Spoon over the sauce so that the fish
is covered. Bring to simmering point, cover
and cook for 12-15 minutes, until the fish
flakes easily when tested with a fork.
Serve in deep soup plates or bowls.

Serve with: Hot crusty wholemeal rolls.

grilled lemon plaice with almonds

*10 minutes
+ marinating*

*270 kcal /1134 kJ per
portion*

*A delicious mixture of smooth and crunchy
textures.*

Serves 4

*450 g /1 lb plaice fillets
juice of 1 lemon
sea salt and freshly ground black pepper
25 g /1 oz butter
1 teaspoon mild paprika
2 tablespoons chopped parsley
75 g /3 oz flaked almonds*

Cut the plaice fillets in half lengthways and
arrange them on a large, flat, heatproof dish,
overlapping as little as possible. Sprinkle with
the lemon juice, season well and leave to
stand for 30 minutes at room temperature.
Heat the grill to high. Beat the butter until it is
soft and gradually beat in the paprika and
parsley.
Dot the plaice with the paprika butter and
put it under the grill for about 7 minutes so it
is cooked through but not browned. Sprinkle
the plaice with the almonds and return it to
the grill for 1 minute for the almonds to
brown. Serve straight from the dish.

Serve with: Dark green vegetables and
boiled (preferably new) potatoes.

monkfish and fennel salad

*25 minutes
+ marinating
+ chilling*

*210 kcal /882 kJ per
portion*

Serves 4

*1 medium-sized fennel bulb
350 g /12 oz tail piece of monkfish
2 small or 1 large lettuce heart
12 stuffed olives*

*For the dressing:
3 tablespoons olive oil
2 tablespoons lemon juice
1 clove garlic, crushed
½ teaspoon fresh tarragon, chopped
½ teaspoon fresh basil, chopped
½ teaspoon fresh chervil, chopped
salt and freshly ground black pepper*

*For the court bouillon:
2 medium-sized carrots, peeled and finely
   chopped
1 medium-sized onion, finely chopped
2 celery stalks, cleaned and chopped
bouquet garni of fresh herbs
2 tablespoons lemon juice
300 ml /½ pint dry white wine
6 black peppercorns, crushed*

Trim the base and the fronds from the fennel.
Slice the bulb finely and put in a bowl. Blend
the dressing ingredients together and pour
over the fennel. Marinate for 2 hours.
Meanwhile put all the court bouillon
ingredients into a saucepan with 600 ml /1 pt
water. Bring to the boil then lower the heat
and simmer for 15 minutes. Cool slightly.
Put the monkfish in a saucepan and strain the
court bouillon over the fish. Bring slowly to
the boil, cover, lower the heat and simmer
for about 10 minutes or until the flesh just
flakes. Carefully remove the fish with a
slotted spoon and leave to cool.
With a sharp knife, cut the cold fish into 4 x
15-mm/1½ x ½-inch pieces and toss with the
fennel and its dressing. Chill for 30 minutes.
Finely shred the lettuce heart and arrange
around the edge of a plate. Pile the fish in the
centre and decorate with olives.

Serve with: New potatoes and tomato salad.

savoury fish with four herbs

*35 minutes
+ cooling*

*265 kcal /1113 kJ per
portion*

*Most mayonnaise is extremely high in fat,
however there are now a few brands of
low-calorie mayonnaise which are
fat-reduced: always use these.*

Serves 6

monkfish and fennel salad

900 g /2 lbs haddock or hake fillets
salt and freshly ground black pepper
juice of 1 large lemon
200 ml /7 fl oz plain yoghurt
3 tablespoons freshly chopped mixed herbs —
    parsley, chervil, tarragon and chives
150 ml /5 fl oz low-calorie mayonnaise

To garnish:
2 medium-sized eggs, hard-boiled and
    quartered
2 firm tomatoes, quartered
a few sprigs of watercress
50 g /2 oz peeled cooked prawns
1 tablespoon freshly chopped parsley

Place the fish in a shallow pan with cold
water to cover, 2 teaspoons salt and 1
tablespoon lemon juice. Bring to simmering
point, cover and poach gently for about 10
minutes or until just cooked. Drain, remove
all skin and bones and flake coarsely.
Put the fish into a bowl and, while it is still
hot, add 2 tablespoons of yoghurt, the
remaining lemon juice, the herbs and salt and
pepper to taste. Mix gently but thoroughly,
cover with cling film and set aside until cold –
about 1 hour.
When ready to serve, pile the fish in the
centre of a serving dish. Combine the
remaining yoghurt with the mayonnaise and
spoon over the fish. Arrange the eggs,
tomatoes and watercress around the fish.
Scatter the prawns over the salad, sprinkle
with the parsley and serve.

Serve with: Garlic bread and a green salad of
crispy lettuce, cucumber and watercress.

jellied gazpacho

`0:00`

| 30 minutes + chilling | 170 kcal /714 kJ per portion |

Serves 6

1 tablespoon gelatine
1 thick slice white bread, crusts removed
½ small green pepper, cored and seeded
1 button onion
225 g /8 oz tomatoes
¼ medium-sized cucumber
1 clove garlic
1 tablespoon wine vinegar
175 ml /6 fl oz tomato juice
salt and freshly ground black pepper

For the filling:
¼ medium-sized cucumber, skinned and seeded
½ small green pepper, cored and seeded
1 medium-sized tomato, blanched, skinned and seeded

To garnish:
6 slices bread
40 g /1½ oz butter, softened
2 cloves garlic
spring onions

Put 3 tablespoons water in a small bowl and sprinkle the gelatine on top. Leave for 5 minutes, then stand in a pan of very hot water and stir until the gelatine has dissolved. Leave to cool.

Break the bread into pieces. Roughly chop the green pepper, onion, tomatoes and cucumber and place in a blender or food processor with the bread, garlic and vinegar. Blend to a purée and then sieve. Stir the tomato juice into the purée and season to taste. Stir in the cooled gelatine.

For the filling, chop the cucumber, green pepper and tomato into small pieces. Stir into the tomato mixture and pour into 6 small oiled moulds. Cover and chill until set.

To make the garnish, heat the oven to 180C/350F/Gas 4. Cut heart shapes from the bread with a biscuit cutter. Mash the butter and crushed garlic together, then heat gently. Pour onto a saucer. Dip the bread into the melted butter to coat both sides. Put on a baking sheet. Bake for about 20 minutes or until crisp and golden. Serve with the chilled jellies, garnished with the spring onions.

jellied gazpacho

spinach pâté

| 30 minutes + chilling | 100 kcal /420 kJ per portion |

This is an unusual, but delicious pâté that is easy to make and always a favourite. Spinach is a rich source of iron and, also, fibre.

Serves 4

225 g /8 oz young spinach leaves, washed
1 tablespoon oil
6 spring onions, finely chopped
2 tablespoons chopped fresh mint leaves
150 g /5 oz curd cheese
salt and freshly ground black pepper
pinch of cayenne pepper
1 tablespoon lemon juice
4 thin slices of lemon, to garnish

Put the spinach in a large pan with only the water that clings to the leaves after washing and cook over moderate heat for 5 minutes until completely tender. Drain well in a colander, pressing with a large spoon to extract as much moisture as possible, then chop it as finely as you can with a sharp pointed knife.

Heat the oil in a pan and sauté the spring

onions over moderate heat for 2-3 minutes, stirring occasionally. Add the chopped mint and spinach and mix well. Remove from the heat and leave to cool.

When the spinach mixture is cool, stir in the curd cheese, salt, pepper, cayenne pepper and lemon juice. Purée in 2 batches in a blender or food processor.

Divide the pâté between 4 individual ramekin dishes and smooth the tops. Cover and chill in the refrigerator for at least 1 hour. Garnish each with a slice of lemon.

Serve with: Granary rolls or toast fingers.

watercress and onion soup

`0:00`

| 30 minutes | 175 kcal /735 kJ per portion |

Serves 4

25 g /1 oz butter
2 medium-sized onions, finely chopped
1 tablespoon flour
600 ml /1 pint chicken stock
¼ teaspoon ground mace
salt and freshly ground black pepper
1 bay leaf
300 ml /½ pint dry white wine
75 g /3 oz watercress, stems and leaves, finely chopped
4 slices of French bread, toasted
50 g /2 oz low-fat hard cheese or Edam, grated

Melt the butter in a saucepan over a low heat. Add the onions and cook, stirring occasionally, until they are golden – about 5 minutes.

Stir in the flour and cook for 1 minute. Add the stock gradually and bring to the boil, stirring, then add the mace, salt and pepper and bay leaf. Lower the heat and simmer, uncovered, for 10 minutes.

Remove the bay leaf. Pour in the wine and add the watercress. Bring the soup to just below boiling point and remove it from the heat.

Put a slice of toasted French bread in each of 4 soup bowls. Sprinkle with the cheese, pour the soup over and serve at once.

carrot soup with yoghurt

carrot soup with yoghurt

0·00

2

45 minutes

110 kcal /462 kJ per portion

The sweetness of carrots is contrasted with the sharp flavours of yoghurt and spices.

Serves 4

1 tablespoon oil
450 g /1 lb carrots, thinly sliced
1 large onion, finely chopped
1 teaspoon ground coriander
1 litre /1¾ pints chicken or light beef stock
salt and freshly ground black pepper
bouquet garni
2 teaspoon cornflour
150 ml /5 fl oz natural yoghurt
1 clove garlic, crushed with a pinch of salt

To garnish:
1 carrot, coarsely grated
flat-leaved parsley sprigs

Heat the oil in a saucepan over a low heat. Stir in the carrots, onion and coriander. Cover and cook gently for 7 minutes. Pour in the stock and bring to the boil. Season and add the bouquet garni. Cover, lower the heat and simmer for 20 minutes until the carrots are soft. Meanwhile, blend the cornflour with the yoghurt in a saucepan. Bring the mixture slowly to the boil, stirring. Simmer for 2 minutes and remove from the heat.

Remove the bouquet garni from the cooked carrots. Purée the carrots in a blender with the cooking liquid, or rub through a vegetable mill, until quite smooth. Stir in the garlic.

Stir the yoghurt into the soup and reheat, without boiling. Serve the soup in heated, individual bowls, garnished with grated carrot and parsley.

Serve with: Rye bread or pumpernickel.

jerusalem artichoke and lemon soup

jerusalem artichoke and lemon soup

55 minutes | 95 kcal /399 kJ per portion

Jerusalem artichokes are another vegetable rich in fibre — and very easy to grow!

Serves 4

1 tablespoon oil
450 g /1 lb Jerusalem artichokes, peeled and thinly sliced
2 medium-sized onions, thinly sliced
900 ml /1½ pints chicken stock
2 thinly pared strips of lemon rind
1 bouquet garni
salt and freshly ground black pepper
2 teaspoons lemon juice (see recipe)
150 g /5 oz natural yoghurt
thinly sliced lemon
2 tablespoons chopped parsley

Heat the oil in a saucepan over a low heat. Stir in the artichokes and onions. Cover and cook gently for 10 minutes. Pour in the stock and bring it to the boil. Add the lemon rind and bouquet garni and season to taste with salt and pepper. Lower the heat and simmer for 20 minutes. Discard the rind and the bouquet garni and purée the soup in a blender or a vegetable mill. Add the 2 teaspoons lemon juice, taste the soup and add more lemon juice if required. Stir in the yoghurt, reheat gently, without boiling, then serve, garnished with the lemon and parsley.

broccoli, raisin and walnut salad

30 minutes + marinating | 145 kcal /609 kJ per portion

For a more luxurious salad, the raisins could be marinated in brandy rather than orange juice.

Serves 4

100 g /4 oz seedless raisins
3 tablespoons orange juice
450 g /1 lb broccoli, cut into florets
salt
2 large carrots, cut into matchstick strips
lettuce leaves, to serve
25 g /1 oz chopped walnuts

For the dressing:
100 ml /3½ fl oz plain yoghurt
1 teaspoon clear honey
salt and freshly ground black pepper

Put the raisins and orange juice in a screw-top jar, replace the lid, shake well and leave to marinate overnight. Shake the jar occasionally, if convenient.
Steam the broccoli florets over boiling, salted water for 6-7 minutes, or until they are barely tender, cool quickly and dry on absorbent paper.
To make the dressing, combine the yoghurt with the honey and add salt and pepper to taste.
Just before serving, drain the raisins and toss them with the broccoli and carrots. Stir in the dressing. Cover a serving dish with lettuce leaves, pile the salad onto the lettuce and garnish with the chopped walnuts.

Serve with: Garlic bread.

broccoli mustard toasts

broccoli mustard toasts

25 minutes | 160 kcal /672 kJ per portion

This unusual dish would make a delicious starter or snack, perhaps served with some chopped ham.

Serves 4

225 g /8 oz fresh or frozen broccoli spears
salt and freshly ground black pepper
4 large slices wholemeal or white bread, crusts removed
40 g /1½ oz butter, softened
½ teaspoon made English mustard
1½ tablespoons lemon juice
lemon twists, to garnish

Heat the grill to high. Bring a saucepan of salted water to the boil and add the broccoli. Bring back to the boil, lower the heat slightly, then cover and simmer gently for 8-10 minutes or until just tender.
Meanwhile, spread 1 side of each slice of bread with some of the butter. Toast the slices on both sides, buttered sides first. Remove from the grill and spread the unbuttered sides with the mustard. Cut each slice in half diagonally and arrange, mustard-side up, on a warmed shallow serving dish.
Drain the broccoli and arrange the spears on the toast, trimming the stalks if necessary to make them fit. Keep hot in a low oven. Put the remaining butter in a small saucepan, together with the lemon juice and salt and pepper to taste. Stir to blend, then heat gently until the butter begins to froth. Immediately pour the butter mixture over the broccoli and serve, garnished with lemon twists.

marrow with peanut and cashew stuffing

1½ hours

355 kcal /1491 kJ per portion

Almonds or brazil nuts could be substituted for the cashews in this tasty vegetarian main course.

Serves 4

1.25 kg /2¾ lbs whole marrow
75 g /3 oz peanuts, shelled and skinned
75 g /3 oz cashew nuts
1 tablespoon oil
1 large onion, finely chopped
1 garlic clove, finely chopped
100 g /4 oz wholemeal breadcrumbs
2 tablespoons chopped parsley
1 tablespoon chopped marjoram
1 tablespoon tomato purée
6 tablespoons dry white wine
salt and freshly ground black pepper

Heat the oven to 200C/400F/Gas 6. Cut off both ends of the marrow and reserve. Scoop out and discard the seeds from the main part. Put the marrow and both reserved ends into a large saucepan containing lightly salted simmering water, bring to the boil, then lower the heat and simmer for 5 minutes. Drain well.
Grind the nuts in a blender or coffee grinder. Heat the oil in a frying-pan over a low heat. Add the onion and garlic and cook until they are soft but not coloured. Remove the pan from the heat and mix in the nuts, breadcrumbs, herbs, tomato purée, wine and seasonings.
Fill the marrow with the stuffing and anchor the ends back on with cocktail sticks. Place the marrow in a large lightly greased casserole, cover with foil or a lid and bake for 1 hour.
To serve, discard the ends, cut the marrow into 4 thick slices and peel it.

Serve with: Green beans and grilled tomatoes.

marrow with peanut and cashew stuffing

cheesy vegetable hotpot

2¼ hours

290 kcal /1218 kJ per portion

A substantial vegetarian main course that needs no other accompaniment.

Serves 4

2 tablespoons oil
2 large carrots, sliced
1 small turnip, diced
2 celery stalks, thinly sliced
12 small leeks, including green tops, cleaned and thickly sliced
25 g /1 oz flour
425 ml /15 fl oz vegetable stock
salt and freshly ground black pepper
1 teaspoon Worcestershire sauce
2 tablespoons chopped fresh parsley
450 g /1 lb potatoes, peeled and sliced
50 g /2 oz grated Cheddar cheese
finely chopped parsley to garnish

Heat the oven to 180C/350F/Gas 4. Heat the oil in a frying-pan and fry the carrots, turnip and celery over a low-to-medium heat for 7-8 minutes, stirring often to prevent them from browning or sticking. Remove the vegetables with a slotted spoon and put them into a 1-litre/2-pint casserole.
Add the leeks to the oil in the pan and fry them for 2-3 minutes, stirring. Add to the casserole.
Stir the flour into the oil remaining in the pan, then gradually pour on the stock, stirring. Bring to the boil, still stirring, then season with salt, pepper and Worcestershire sauce. Lower the heat and simmer for 3 minutes, then mix in the parsley. Pour the sauce over the vegetables in the casserole and toss carefully to mix.
Arrange the sliced potatoes in overlapping circles on top of the vegetables. Cover the casserole with a lid or with foil, stand it on a baking sheet and cook for 1½ hours, or until the potatoes are tender. Heat the grill to high. Sprinkle the cheese over the potatoes and grill until well browned. Garnish with parsley and serve.

vegetables with crispy almonds

40 minutes

415 kcal /1743 kJ per portion

Cooking the vegetables in this way keeps them crisp and delicious.

Serves 4

1 small cauliflower, broken into small florets
2 medium-sized green peppers, seeded and sliced
1 medium-sized onion, finely chopped
225 g /8 oz bean sprouts, washed
2 tablespoons oil
1 clove garlic, chopped
1 teaspoon ground ginger
200 g /7 oz almonds, blanched
2 tablespoons cornflour
2 tablespoons soy sauce
4 tablespoons sherry
2 tablespoons tomato purée
300 ml /½ pint stock
salt and freshly ground black pepper

Prepare the vegetables and put on one side. Heat the oil in a frying-pan or wok and fry the garlic until it begins to sizzle. Add the cauliflower, peppers and onions and stir-fry over a moderate heat for 2 minutes. Sprinkle in the ginger and add the bean sprouts and almonds and cook for 1 minute more.
Put the cornflour in a bowl and mix in the soy sauce, sherry and tomato purée to make a smooth paste. Add the stock, whisking it in thoroughly.
Stir this cornflour mixture into the pan. Stir everything together, then cover and cook on a low heat for 10 minutes, stirring occasionally. Serve at once.

Serve with: Boiled brown rice.

mixed vegetable curry

0·00

40 minutes

255 kcal /1071 kJ per portion

It is worth seeking out the spices for this curry dish — the flavour is delicious.

Serves 4

450 g /1 lb potatoes, cubed
450 g /1 lb leeks, trimmed and washed
1 small cauliflower, broken into small florets
100 g /4 oz shelled peas
2 tablespoons oil
1 clove garlic, peeled and crushed
1 medium-sized onion, peeled and chopped
1 tablespoon ground cumin
½ teaspoon turmeric
½ teaspoon powdered fenugreek
½ teaspoon white mustard seed
1 bay leaf
225 g /8 oz canned tomatoes
400 ml /14 fl oz water
2 teaspoons garam masala
salt and freshly ground black pepper

Cook the potatoes in boiling salted water for about 10 minutes. Meanwhile cut the leeks into 15-mm/½-inch pieces. Add the leeks, cauliflower florets and peas to the potato. Continue cooking until all the vegetables are just tender. Drain.
Heat the oil in a large saucepan and add the garlic and onion. Cook gently for 10 minutes, then stir in the ground cumin, turmeric, fenugreek and mustard. Cook for 2-3 minutes, stirring frequently.
Add the bay leaf, tomatoes and the water to the onion and spices. Let the mixture simmer gently for 15 minutes, stirring from time to time.
Stir in the garam masala and add the drained vegetables, being careful not to break them. Taste and season with salt and pepper. Serve at once.

Serve with: Boiled rice, plain yoghurt and mango chutney or lime pickle.

cucumber ring

cucumber ring

2 hours + setting

180 kcal /756 kJ per portion

Serves 4

½ large cucumber, peeled, seeded and finely
  chopped
2 tablespoons tarragon or white wine vinegar
salt and freshly ground black pepper
450 g /1 lb cottage cheese
150 ml /5 fl oz natural yoghurt
2 teaspoons powdered gelatine
3 tablespoons water
3 spring onions, finely chopped (including the
  green parts)
2 tablespoons snipped chives
3 tablespoons each finely chopped parsley
  and watercress sprigs

For the filling:
small wedges of tomato and stoned black
  olives

Place the cucumber in a bowl, sprinkle with
the vinegar and 1 tablespoon salt and toss
well. Tip into a sieve, weight down with a
plate and leave to drain for at least 1 hour.
Remove the plate and press the cucumber
gently to extract any remaining liquid.
Mix together the cottage cheese and yoghurt
and process, a batch at a time, in a blender or
food processor. Put this into a large bowl.
Sprinkle the gelatine over the water in a
small, heavy-based saucepan and leave to
soak for 5 minutes. Set the pan over a very
low heat for 2-3 minutes until the gelatine is
completely dissolved. Remove from the heat.
Stir a few spoonfuls of cheese mixture into
the dissolved gelatine, then pour this on to
the mixture in the bowl, stirring continuously.
When the gelatine has been mixed in, fold in
the cucumber, spring onions, chives, parsley
and watercress. Season generously with
pepper.
Pour the mixture into a lightly oiled
700-ml/1¼-pint ring mould; smooth the
surface, cover with cling film and leave in the
refrigerator for 8 hours or overnight to set.
Put a serving plate upside down over the
mould, turn them over and give a firm shake
to release the cucumber ring. Fill the centre
with wedges of tomato and stoned black
olives.

yoghurt broad beans

20 minutes + chilling

120 kcal /504 kJ per portion

Serves 4

10-cm /4-inch piece of cucumber, quartered
  and seeded
salt and freshly ground black pepper
450 g /1 lb shelled broad beans
1 tablespoon oil
2 teaspoons lemon juice
salt and freshly ground black pepper
75 g /3 oz curd cheese
150 ml /5 fl oz natural yoghurt
1-2 tablespoons freshly chopped chives
very thinly sliced onion rings, to garnish

Chop the cucumber into small dice; place in a
sieve in layers, sprinkling salt between each
layer. Set aside.
Cook the beans briefly in boiling, lightly
salted water until just tender. Meanwhile
combine the oil and lemon juice in a mixing
bowl with salt and pepper to taste and whisk
well with a fork.
Drain the cooked beans, add to the bowl
with the dressing, turning to coat them. Set
aside.
With a wooden spoon, beat together the
curd cheese and 1 tablespoon of the yoghurt
until smoothly blended. Beat in the
remaining yoghurt, and stir in the chives.
Rinse the cucumber in cold water, drain and
pat dry with absorbent paper. Stir the
cucumber into the yoghurt dressing, then
spoon this over the beans. Stir gently, but
thoroughly, and season.
Turn the salad into a serving dish, cover and
chill in the refrigerator for 20-30 minutes.
Garnish with onion rings.

spinach pancakes

40 minutes

100 kcal /420 kJ per pancake

These pancakes could be served with a filling
of cottage cheese mixed with chives or a
home-made tomato sauce as a starter or a
main course.

Makes 8 pancakes

175 g /6 oz spinach, washed, stalks and large
  midribs removed
oil or lard for frying

For the batter:
100 g /4 oz plain flour
½ teaspoon freshly grated nutmeg
salt
1 egg
125 ml /4 fl oz milk
125 ml /4 fl oz water

Put the spinach in a large pan with only the
water that clings to the leaves after washing
and cook over moderate heat for 5 minutes
until completely tender. Drain well in a
colander, pressing with a large spoon to
extract as much moisture as possible, then
chop the spinach as finely as you can with a
sharp pointed knife.
Make the batter: sift flour, nutmeg and salt
into a bowl, make a well in the centre and
add the egg, milk and water. Using a wire
whisk, gradually draw the flour into the
liquid keeping the batter completely smooth.
When the flour is completely incorporated,
stir in the chopped spinach.
Heat a little oil in an 18-cm/7-inch frying-pan.
Remove from the heat, pour in 2 tablespoons
of the batter and tilt the pan until the batter
covers the base evenly. Return to the heat
and cook until the top looks dry and the
underside is golden brown. Loosen the edge
with a palette knife and shake the pan, then
toss the pancake over and cook on the other
side for a further 20-30 seconds until golden.
Lift the pancake on to a sheet of greaseproof
paper and keep warm.
Continue making pancakes in the same way,
interleaving them with greaseproof paper.
Stir the batter frequently and grease the pan
with more oil as necessary.

spinach pancakes

cover, lower the heat and simmer very gently for 20-30 minutes, until the vegetables are tender.

Heat the oven to 190C/375F/Gas 5. Drain the vegetables well, mash and return them to the saucepan. Stir them constantly over gentle heat to get rid of excess moisture. Stir in the butter and when melted, beat in the breadcrumbs and egg yolks. Check the seasoning.

Pack half the mixture into a greased 900-ml/1½-pint ovenproof basin. Scatter in the herbs and cover with the remaining vegetable mixture. Bake for 30 minutes. Turn the mould out carefully onto a serving plate and serve.

Serve with: Sliced meat and gravy.

warm spinach salad

herbed swede and carrot mould

1¼ hours

140 kcal/588 kJ per portion

Swede is all too often a neglected vegetable, which is a pity. When in season, it is generally very reasonably priced, and it is a good source of fibre.

Serves 6

450 g/1 lb swede, finely chopped
450 g/1 lb carrots, finely chopped
1 small onion, finely chopped
salt and freshly ground black pepper
15 g/½ oz butter
25 g/1 oz fresh breadcrumbs
2 medium-sized egg yolks, beaten
2 tablespoons chopped fresh mixed herbs
    (such as mint, chives, rosemary and thyme)

Put the swede, carrots and onion in a large saucepan. Add water just to cover and season with salt and pepper. Bring to the boil,

warm spinach salad

30 minutes + cooling

115 kcal/483 kJ per portion (6 servings)

Serves 4-6

1 kg/2¼ lbs spinach, washed, stalks and large
    midribs removed
2 tablespoons vegetable oil
1 medium-sized onion, coarsely chopped
salt and freshly ground black pepper
500 ml/18 fl oz natural yoghurt

Shred the spinach. Heat the oil in a large saucepan over medium-low heat. Fry the onion, stirring occasionally, until it is soft. Add the spinach and cook, stirring occasionally, until it reduces to a tender mass. Season with salt and pepper and transfer to a dish. Beat the yoghurt, stir it into the spinach and let the mixture cool for about 15 minutes before serving.

Serve with: Grilled meat or fish.

alfalfa and chicory salad

alfalfa and chicory salad

15 minutes

100 kcal /420 kJ per portion

Alfalfa sprouts resemble very thin beansprouts and have a nutty taste. They are a good source of vitamin C.

Serves 4

1 small lettuce
100 g /4 oz alfalfa sprouts
1 head chicory, thinly sliced
1 small green pepper, seeded and cut into
  15-mm/$\frac{1}{2}$-inch cubes
sprig of fresh tarragon, to garnish (optional)

For the dressing:
$\frac{1}{2}$ teaspoon made English mustard
1 teaspoon sugar
2 teaspoons white wine vinegar
150 ml /5 fl oz single cream
1 teaspoon finely chopped fresh tarragon
salt and freshly ground black pepper

Make the dressing: mix together the mustard, sugar and vinegar in a bowl until smooth. Gradually stir in the cream until well blended, then mid in the tarragon and season to taste with salt and pepper. Cover the bowl and refrigerate until required. Discard any outer damaged leaves of the lettuce, then shred the rest and place in a large salad bowl. Add the alfalfa sprouts, chicory and green pepper to the salad bowl and mix gently.
Pour the dressing over the salad and toss gently to coat. Garnish with a sprig of fresh tarragon, if liked, and serve at once.

Serve with: Cold fish such as salmon or a fish salad.

lettuce, bacon and radish salad

25 minutes | 180 kcal/756 kJ per portion

This is another main course salad; substitute curly endive or chicory for the lettuce when you can find them.

Serves 4

200 g /7 oz streaky bacon rashers, derinded
2 large heads of round lettuce, washed and
　　chilled
12 medium-sized radishes, thinly sliced
125 ml /4 fl oz red wine vinegar
1½ teaspoons sugar
½ teaspoon grated horseradish
¼ teaspoon freshly ground black pepper
12 spring onions, coarsely chopped
1 hard-boiled egg yolk, sieved

Cook the bacon in a frying-pan over moderate heat until crisp. Drain on absorbent paper.
Meanwhile, tear the cold, crisp lettuce into a serving bowl. Slice the radishes thinly and add them to the bowl.
Drain off the fat from the frying-pan and then add the vinegar, sugar, horseradish and pepper to the pan. Cook over medium heat until the mixture begins to bubble. Stir in the spring onions for 1 minute, then pour over the salad. Toss to mix. Crumble the bacon on top of the salad and top with the sieved egg yolk.

chinese cabbage, carrot and beansprout salad

chinese cabbage, carrot and beansprout salad

25 minutes | 130 kcal/546 kJ per portion

Chinese cabbage is widely available in greengrocers and supermarkets. It is crispy and delicious; use it in place of lettuce in an ordinary green salad.

Serves 4

½ head Chinese cabbage, finely shredded
100 g /4 oz beansprouts
100 g /4 oz carrots, coarsely grated
2 tablespoons sesame seeds

For the dressing:
2 tablespoons oil
juice of 1 lemon
1 tablespoon soy sauce
1 teaspoon honey
1 garlic clove, crushed with a pinch of salt
½ teaspoon ground ginger

In a salad bowl, combine the Chinese cabbage, beansprouts and carrots.
Beat the ingredients for the dressing together and fold them into the salad.
Place the sesame seeds in a dry, heavy frying-pan over a moderate heat and stir until they brown. Remove the pan from the heat and scatter the toasted seeds over the salad. Serve at once, while the seeds are still warm and the salad is crisp.

jerusalem artichoke and sausage salad

jerusalem artichoke and sausage salad

`0:00`

45 minutes + cooling

235 kcal/987 kJ per portion

2

A main course salad; omit the sausage for a vegetarian dish, or if you want to reduce the calories even further.

Serves 4

1 tablespoon lemon juice
700 g /1½ lbs Jerusalem artichokes
salt
1 large orange
350 g /12 oz tomatoes, chopped
1 medium-sized green pepper, seeded and
    diced
1 medium-sized red pepper, seeded and diced
8 green olives, halved and stoned
100 g /4 oz lean garlic sausage, cut into
    15-mm /½-inch dice
3 tablespoons chopped parsley to garnish

For the dressing:
3 tablespoons olive oil
2 tablespoons white wine vinegar
2 teaspoons tomato purée
¼ teaspoon Tabasco sauce
1 garlic clove, crushed with a pinch of salt

Fill a large bowl with water and add the lemon juice. Peel the artichokes, cut them into 15-mm/½-inch dice and immediately drop them into the bowl of acidulated water to prevent discolouration. When all the artichokes have been prepared, drain them and place in a steamer. Steam for 7 minutes over boiling, salted water.
Cut the peel and pith from the orange and chop the flesh. Mix together the oil, vinegar, tomato purée, Tabasco sauce and garlic to make the dressing. Fold this into the artichokes while they are still warm. Leave them to get cold – about 1 hour.
Mix the orange, tomatoes, green and red peppers, olives and sausage into the artichokes. Put the salad into a serving bowl and sprinkle it with the chopped parsley. Serve at once.

artichoke and watercress salad

artichoke and
watercress salad

0:00	2
20 minutes	*100 kcal /420 kJ per portion*

The blue cheese dressing gives this salad an added tangy flavour. Serve it as a starter or as an accompaniment to a main course. Watercress is a good source of vitamin A.

Serves 4

400 g /14 oz can artichoke hearts, drained
2 bunches watercress, separated into sprigs
4 large tomatoes, thinly sliced
½ medium-sized cucumber, thinly sliced
mild paprika, to garnish

For the dressing:
50 g /2 oz Danish blue cheese
150 ml /5 fl oz natural yoghurt
2 tablespoon milk
1 tablespoon lemon juice
1-1½ teaspoons Worcestershire sauce
salt and freshly ground black pepper

First make the dressing: mash the cheese in a small bowl with a fork, then gradually blend in 2 tablespoons of the yoghurt. Beat until smooth, then beat in the remaining yoghurt, the milk and lemon juice. Season to taste with Worcestershire sauce, salt and pepper. Place 1 artichoke heart in the centre of 4 individual plates. Surround with a border of watercress sprigs and decorate with slices of tomato and cucumber. Cut any remaining artichoke hearts into pieces and place among the watercress.
Pour a generous spoonful of the dressing on the edge of each salad. Sprinkle the centre of the cheese dressing with paprika and serve at once.

Serve with: Grilled chops or chicken pieces.

kibbutz citrus carrot salad

15 minutes + cooling

65 kcal /273 kJ per portion

This amount of carrots provides a significant quantity of fibre — a good boost to the daily intake.

Serves 6

1 kg /2¼ lbs carrots
freshly squeezed juice of 3 large oranges
freshly squeezed juice of 2 lemons
2 teaspoons honey
slices of orange or lemon to serve

Grate the carrots into a large bowl. Strain the orange and lemon juice to remove the pips and pour over the carrots. Add 125 ml/4 fl oz water and stir in the honey.
Cover the bowl and refrigerate for at least 2 hours, for the flavours to mingle, before serving. Decorate with slices of citrus fruits.

celeriac salad dijonnaise

20 minutes

60 kcal /252 kJ per portion (6 servings)

Serves 4-6

700 g /1½ lbs celeriac

For the dressing:
3 tablespoons natural yoghurt
2 tablespoons oil
1 teaspoon Dijon mustard
1 garlic clove, crushed with a pinch of salt
3 tablespoons chopped parsley

Peel the celeriac and cut it into matchstick-sized pieces. Drop the pieces into a large pan of boiling, salted water. Boil for 2 minutes and drain.
Beat together the yoghurt, oil, mustard, garlic and parsley to make the dressing and fold it into the celeriac while it is still hot. Serve the salad hot or cold.

Serve with: A selection of cold meats or as a starter with grated carrots and cubed beetroot.

beetroot and orange salad

20 minutes

150 kcal /630 kJ per portion

Beetroot and orange are surprisingly complementary; try stirring a spoonful of orange juice into Borsch, or garnishing it with orange segments or slices.

Serves 4

4 small cooked beetroots
2 oranges
1 lettuce, washed
2 large tomatoes, sliced
3-4 teaspoons finely chopped walnuts

For the dressing:
1 teaspoon finely chopped onion
1 teaspoon snipped chives
salt and freshly ground black pepper
½ teaspoon made English mustard
good pinch of caster sugar
2 tablespoons oil
1 tablespoon wine vinegar
dash of Worcestershire sauce

Skin the beetroots and slice them thinly. Peel the oranges over a small bowl to catch any juice. Slice them into thin rings.
Put the lettuce leaves on a serving dish and then arrange the beetroot and orange slices alternately in a ring on top of the lettuce. Place overlapping slices of tomato in the centre of the dish and sprinkle with the walnuts.
Make the dressing by mixing the onion, chives, salt and pepper, mustard and caster sugar together with the reserved orange juice. Using a fork, whisk in the oil, vinegar and Worcestershire sauce and whisk until well blended. Spoon the dressing over the salad and serve at once.

Serve with: Cold meats or a selection of salads.

beetroot and orange salad

carrot, fennel and pepper salad

35 minutes

130 kcal /546 kJ per portion

This is a crunchy fresh-tasting salad

Serves 4

225 g /8 oz carrots, grated
225 g /8 oz fennel, chopped
2 medium-sized green peppers, seeded and diced
1 small cooking apple, cored and chopped
2 tablespoons poppy seeds

For the dressing:
2 tablespoons oil
2 tablespoons white wine vinegar
1 garlic clove, crushed with a pinch of salt
freshly ground black pepper

Mix the vegetables and apple in a bowl with the poppy seeds.
To make the dressing, beat the oil, vinegar, garlic and pepper together until they emulsify, and fold into the salad. Leave the tossed salad to stand for 15 minutes before serving.

Serve with: Cold meat and lettuce leaves.

grapefruit, celery and mint salad

15 minutes + chilling

100 kcal /420 kJ per portion

This makes a lovely fresh starter or an any-time snack.

Serves 4

2 large grapefruits
2 heads celery
4 teaspoons chopped fresh mint
2 tablespoons seedless raisins
4 sprigs of mint, to garnish

For the dressing:
150 ml /5 fl oz natural yoghurt
1 tablespoon olive oil
1 tablespoon orange juice
salt and freshly ground black pepper

Cut each grapefruit in half, in a zig-zag. Scoop out the flesh, using a curved grapefruit knife. Reserve the shells in the refrigerator. Discard the pith, membranes and pips and put the grapefruit flesh into a bowl.
Remove and discard the outer stalks of the celery, leaving only the tender, yellow 'hearts' (reserve the outer stalks for another dish or soup). Cut the celery hearts into 5-mm /¼-inch slices and add to the grapefruit, together with the chopped mint and raisins. Toss well.
Make the dressing, stir together the yoghurt, oil and orange juice and season to taste with salt and pepper.
Add the dressing to the salad, toss well and pile into the grapefruit shells. Refrigerate the filled shells for 30 minutes. Garnish with mint sprigs and serve.

Serve with: Melba toast.

grapefruit and celery salad

watercress and grapefruit salad

25 minutes

155 kcal /651 kJ per portion

Serves 4

50 g /2 oz split almonds
2 pink grapefruits, divided into segments
2 bunches watercress, stalks removed

For the dressing:
1 teaspoon finely chopped onion
½ teaspoon sugar
juice of 1 fresh lime
2 tablespoons olive oil
salt and freshly ground black pepper

Heat the grill to moderate and spread the almonds in the grill pan. Toast them for 8-10 minutes, turning them from time to time, until they are golden brown.
To make the dressing: put the onion, sugar, lime juice and olive oil in a salad bowl. Whisk with a fork until the dressing is thick and all the ingredients are thoroughly combined. Season with salt and pepper. Stir the grapefruit segments and any juice reserved from this preparation into the dressing. Add the watercress leaves and toss together. Sprinkle the toasted almonds over the salad and serve at once.

Serve with: Slices of cold tongue or poultry; particularly duck.

carrot, fennel and pepper salad

spicy bean pâté

15 minutes + chilling

85 kcal /357 kJ per portion

This is an unusual pâté, but quite delicious and very filling.

Serves 4

425 g /15 oz can red kidney beans
1 clove garlic, crushed (optional)
1 tablespoon tomato purée
1 teaspoon Worcestershire sauce
1 teaspoon lemon juice
few drops of Tabasco
salt and freshly ground black pepper
parsley sprigs, to garnish

Drain the beans, reserving the liquid from the can. Put all the ingredients into a blender or food processor and blend to a smooth paste; it will be flecked with pieces of bean skin. Alternatively, place all the ingredients in a bowl, pound them with the end of a rolling pin, then mash thoroughly with a fork. If the mixture is too thick, add 2-3 tablespoons of the reserved liquid from the can. Taste and adjust seasoning.

Pack the pâté into 4 small ramekins or other individual dishes and smooth the surface of each with a small knife. Serve the pâté cold or chilled, garnished with parsley sprigs.

Serve with: Toast or vegetable crudités.

spiced chick-peas with potatoes

2¼ hours
+ overnight
soaking

365 kcal/1533 kJ per
portion

You could use canned chick-peas if you do not
want to be bothered with the soaking and
lengthy cooking.

Serves 4

250 g /9 oz chick-peas
4 medium-sized potatoes, scrubbed
1 teaspoon cumin seeds
5 black peppercorns
2 cardamom pods
2 cloves
2.5-cm /1-inch piece of cinnamon
1½ tablespoons vegetable oil
1 medium-sized onion, chopped
2.5-cm /1-inch piece of fresh root ginger,
    finely grated
¼ teaspoon chilli powder
1 green chilli, seeded and chopped (optional)
pinch of sugar
salt
1 tablespoon chopped coriander leaves, to
    garnish (optional)

Wash the chick-peas well, cover them with
plenty of water and leave them to soak
overnight. Put them with their soaking water
in a saucepan. Bring the water to the boil,
lower the heat and simmer for 1½-2 hours or
until the peas are soft. Drain off the liquid
and put the chick-peas to one side.
Meanwhile, boil the potatoes in their skins
until they are just tender. Drain and allow
them to cool, then peel and cut them into
4-cm/1½-inch cubes.
Pound the cumin seeds, peppercorns,
cardamom pods, cloves and cinnamon in a
mortar and pestle or grind them to powder in
an electric coffee grinder.
Heat the oil in a frying-pan over medium-low
heat. When hot, add the onion and fry until it
is soft but not coloured. Add the grated
ginger, chilli powder, the ground spices and
chopped chilli, if used, and fry for 2-3
minutes.
Add the chick-peas, potatoes, sugar and salt
to taste. Mix well and cook for 5 minutes. Put
the mixture in a serving dish, sprinkle with

chopped coriander, if using, and serve hot or
warm.

Serve with: Indian bread such as chapatis or
Paratha.

brown bean soup

2 hours
+ overnight
soaking

310 kcal/1302 kJ per
portion

Serves 6

450 g /1 lb red kidney beans, soaked overnight
4 cloves
6 black peppercorns
1 bay leaf
2 medium-sized leeks, cleaned and sliced
250 g /9 oz potatoes, diced
2 rashers streaky bacon
1 large onion, chopped
1 tablespoon curry powder
few drops of Worcestershire sauce
salt and freshly ground black pepper

Put the drained beans into a heavy saucepan,
pour in water to cover and add the cloves,
peppercorns, and bay leaf. Bring to the boil
and boil rapidly for 10 minutes, then lower
the heat and simmer for 1 hour. Add the leeks
and potatoes and simmer for another 30
minutes.
Cook the bacon in a frying-pan over medium
heat until crisp, remove from the pan and cut
into small pieces. Reserve. Add the onion to
the fat remaining in the frying-pan and cook
until transparent. Stir in the curry powder,
cook for 2 minutes and then remove the pan
from the heat.
Discard the cloves, peppercorns and bay
leaf, then mash the contents of the saucepan
and rub it through a sieve. Return the mixture
to the pan and simmer for 20 minutes or until
the soup has thickened. Add the curry
powder mixture, Worcestershire sauce and
salt and pepper to taste. Serve in individual
bowls with the chopped bacon sprinkled on
top.

Serve with: Chunks of French bread.

home-made baked beans

2 hours
+ overnight
soaking

210 kcal/882 kJ per
portion

Home-made baked beans are infinitely
superior to the canned variety and very little
trouble to make.

Serves 4

200 g /7 oz dried haricot beans, rinsed and
    soaked overnight in cold water
2 tablespoons oil
salt and freshly ground black pepper
1 medium-sized onion, chopped
1 teaspoon tomato purée
225 g /8 oz canned, or blanched, skinned fresh
    tomatoes
pinch of thyme
pinch of crumbled bay leaf
pinch of nutmeg
¼ teaspoon chopped parsley

Drain the beans and dry them with a
tea-cloth. Heat 1 tablespoon oil in a saucepan
over medium heat, add the beans and stir to
coat them with oil. Barely cover the beans
with boiling water and leave them to simmer
gently, covered, for 1½ hours, adding more
water as necessary. Five minutes before they
are cooked, add salt.
Meanwhile, heat the rest of the oil in another
saucepan over low heat and sauté the onion
until soft but not coloured. Add the tomato
purée, stir, and add the tomatoes, thyme, bay
leaf and nutmeg. Cover and cook over very
low heat for about 45 minutes.
Drain the beans, return them to their pan and
strain the tomato sauce over them. Cook
them gently for a further 10 minutes, check
the seasoning and serve.

Serve with: Roast lamb or on slices of toast
for a snack.

mixed bean casserole

2¾ hours
+ overnight
soaking

265 kcal /1113 kJ per
portion

*This filling casserole makes a meal on its own.
Serve with thick grilled bacon rashers if you
want some meat.*

Serves 4

100 g /4 oz haricot beans
100 g /4 oz borlotti (brown) beans
100 g /4 oz black-eyed beans
1 green pepper, seeded
2 tablespoons vegetable oil
1 large onion, chopped
1 small head celery, chopped
2 cloves garlic, crushed
800 g /1 lb 12 oz can tomatoes
425 ml /15 fl oz water
1 teaspoon yeast extract
2 teaspoons dried oregano
salt and freshly ground black pepper

Put the haricot beans into a bowl and the
borlotti and black-eyed beans together in
another. Cover both of them with cold water
and leave to soak overnight.
Drain the borlotti and black-eyed beans,
rinse under cold running water, then put
them into a large saucepan and cover with
fresh water. Bring to the boil and cook for 15
minutes.
Drain and rinse the haricot beans, add to the
pan with the other beans and bring back to
the boil. Lower the heat, cover and cook for a
further 30 minutes.
Meanwhile, cut a few slices from the green
pepper and reserve for the garnish. Chop the
remainder.
Heat the oil in a large heavy-based pan and
fry the onion, celery, the chopped green
pepper and garlic for 10 minutes over a low
heat.
Add the tomatoes and water, then stir in the
yeast extract and add the oregano and salt
and pepper to taste. Bring to the boil.
Drain the beans, add to the pan of
vegetables, cover and cook gently for 1 hour
or until the beans are very tender. Taste and
adjust the seasoning, if necessary. Transfer to
a warmed serving dish and serve garnished
with the reserved green pepper rings.

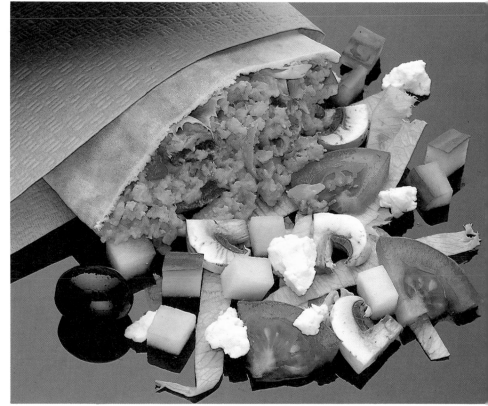

pulse-filled pittas

pulse-filled pittas

50 minutes

405 kcal /1701 kJ per
portion

*Pitta bread is widely available in supermarkets
and is ideal for healthy, filling snacks such as
this one.*

Serves 4

1 tablespoon oil
1 medium-sized onion, finely chopped
100 g /4 oz button mushrooms, thinly sliced
2 teaspoons ground cumin
250 g /9 oz split red lentils
450 ml /16 fl oz chicken, ham or vegetable
    stock
2 tablespoons lemon juice
1 tablespoon finely chopped fresh parsley
salt and freshly ground black pepper
4 pitta breads
4 tomatoes, thinly sliced

Heat the oil in a.saucepan. Add the onion and
fry gently for 3-4 minutes until soft but not
coloured. Add the mushrooms and cumin
and fry for a further 2 minutes, stirring.
Add the lentils and stock to the pan and bring
to the boil, then reduce the heat to very low.
Cover and barely simmer for 20-30 minutes,
stirring occasionally, until the lentils are soft
and the liquid has been absorbed. Add the
lemon juice and parsley to the lentils and
season to taste with salt and pepper. Keep
warm over low heat, stirring occasionally
until the mixture is really thick.
Dampen the pitta breads by sprinkling them
all over with cold water, then toast them
under a hot grill for 2-3 minutes on each side,
until just crisp. Cut them in half, and ease
open with a round-bladed knife. Divide the
lentil mixture between the pitta 'pockets'
and slip a few tomato slices into each one.
Serve at once.

two-bean salad

1¼ hours
+ cooling

260 kcal /1092 kJ per
portion

Serves 4

100 g /4 oz dried red kidney beans, soaked
    overnight
100 g /4 oz dried haricot beans, soaked
    overnight
1 small onion, chopped
1 bay leaf
2 large celery stalks, thinly sliced
1 green pepper, seeded and diced

For the dressing:
4 tablespoons olive oil
2 tablespoons wine vinegar
1 clove garlic, crushed
salt and freshly ground black pepper

Drain the kidney beans. Transfer to a
saucepan, cover with water and bring to the
boil. Boil vigorously for 10 minutes, then add
the haricot beans together with their soaking
liquid. Add the onion and bay leaf and bring
back to the boil. Lower the heat, half cover
with a lid and simmer for about 1 hour until
the beans are tender.
Meanwhile, make the dressing; put the
ingredients in a screw-top jar, with salt and
pepper to taste. Replace the lid firmly and
shake well to mix.
Drain the beans and discard the cooking
liquid and bay leaf. Transfer to a serving dish
and pour over the dressing, while the beans
are still warm. Mix well and leave to stand for
at least 1 hour or overnight.
Add the celery and diced pepper to the
beans, taste and adjust seasoning and mix
well. Serve.

Serve with: Cold meats or assorted cold
salads and garlic bread.

two-bean salad

lentil layer pie

1¼ hours

235 kcal /987 kJ per portion

Serves 4

100 g /4 oz split red lentils
1 large onion, chopped
¼ teaspoon dried basil
¼ teaspoon dried thyme
225 g /8 oz can tomatoes
425 ml /15 fl oz beef stock (or yeast extract plus water)
salt and freshly ground black pepper
15 g /½ oz butter
50 g /2 oz fresh wholemeal breadcrumbs
4 hard-boiled eggs, sliced

Heat the oven to 190C/375F/Gas 5 and grease a 1.1-litre/2-pint baking dish.
Put the lentils, onion, herbs, tomatoes and stock into a pan. Season with salt and pepper and bring to the boil. Lower the heat and cook gently for 15-20 minutes, stirring occasionally until the lentils are just tender. The liquid will not be completely absorbed. Meanwhile, melt the butter in a separate pan, remove from the heat and stir in all but 2 tablespoons of the breadcrumbs. Season with salt and pepper.
Cover the base of the prepared dish with a layer of the lentil mixture then a layer of fried breadcrumbs and a layer of sliced eggs. Continue these layers until all the ingredients are used, finishing with a layer of lentils. Sprinkle the remaining breadcrumbs on top. Bake near the top of the oven for 25-30 minutes until the crumbs are browned. Serve at once, straight from the dish.

Serve with: Green salad.

spiced lentils

1½ hours

215 kcal /903 kJ per portion

Serves 4

225 g /8 oz lentils
1 small cauliflower, broken into florets
3 radishes, cut in 15-mm /½-inch slices
3 courgettes, cut in 2.5cm /1 inch slices
1 teaspoon sugar
salt
1 tablespoon oil
½ teaspoon black mustard seeds
1 green chilli, slightly slit
1 dried red chilli, slightly slit
2.5-cm /1-inch fresh ginger root, peeled and chopped

Wash the lentils and place them in a saucepan. Cover with water, to a depth of 5-cm/2-inch, bring to the boil, lower the heat and simmer for 50-60 minutes, until the lentils are almost tender. Add water to keep them just covered as necessary.
Add the cauliflower, radishes and courgettes and cook until they and the lentils are completely tender – about 10 minutes. Add the sugar and salt to taste and remove the saucepan from the heat.
Heat the oil in a small frying-pan over medium heat. Add the black mustard seeds and when they begin to pop up, add the prepared chillis and chopped ginger. Stir the spices for 1 minute. Remove the chillis, if they will be too hot for you, then mix the spices thoroughly into the lentils and vegetables and serve at once.

Serve with: Boiled brown rice or as part of an Indian meal.

spiced lentils

chick-pea and yoghurt dip

0·00

15 minutes

65 kcal /273 kJ per portion (6 servings)

If you prefer, cook chick-peas for this dip; drain them, reserving a little of the cooking liquor to thin down the purée (see method).

Serves 4-6

225 g /8 oz canned chick-peas, drained
125 ml /4 fl oz natural yoghurt
juice of 1 lemon
1 teaspoon crushed dried mint
salt and freshly ground black pepper
zest of ½ lemon, to garnish

Purée the first 4 ingredients together in a blender or food processor, thinning the mixture down with a little water (or reserved chick-pea cooking water, if available) if it is too thick. Season. Cover and chill until needed.
Serve garnished with lemon zest, coarsely grated or cut into fine strips.

Serve with: Hot pitta bread, fingers of toast or corn chips.

chick-pea and yoghurt dip

pasta to serve with sauces

255 kcal/1071kJ per 75g /3 oz serving

Choose fresh, wholemeal pasta whenever possible. Fresh pasta is easy to find now; most supermarkets, as well as Italian delicatessens stock it. For a main course allow about 75 g/3 oz pasta per person; a little less for a starter. Drop it into a large pan of boiling salted water; 1 tablespoon olive oil or a good knob of butter added to the water will prevent the pasta from sticking together, and also helps to prevent the water from boiling over.

The length of cooking time depends on the thickness and the shape of the pasta. The thinnest noodles will take no more than 30 seconds once the water has come back to the boil. Thicker tagliatelle or pasta twists will take 3-5 minutes. It is cooked when it is *al dente* – tender, but still slightly resistant to the bite. Drain it quickly and serve at once with the sauce of your choice.

Fresh pasta freezes very successfully. Buy extra and freeze it in manageable quantities for up to 6 months. You can cook it straight from the freezer. Use fresh pasta within 4 days of buying it, keeping it in the refrigerator in a sealed polythene bag to prevent it drying out.

pasta types; noodles with walnut and anchovy sauce; spirals with tomato sauce

walnut and anchovy sauce

20 minutes | 130 kcal /546 kJ per portion (6 servings)

Stir 1 tablespoon walnut oil into cooked pasta to serve with this sauce. The flavours will be complementary.

Serves 4-6

150 ml /5 fl oz natural yoghurt
150 g /5 oz ricotta cheese
2 cloves garlic, crushed
6 anchovy fillets, pounded
50 g /2 oz shelled walnuts, broken into small
    pieces
freshly ground black pepper

Mix together the yoghurt and ricotta, mashing the cheese well and beating the ingredients together thoroughly.
Add the garlic cloves, anchovy and walnuts and put in a small pan. Bring to bubbling point over a medium heat, then lower the heat and simmer very gently while you cook some pasta.
Serve poured over pasta with plenty of black pepper.

Serve with: Wholemeal ribbon noodles.

tomato sauce

30 minutes | 40 kcal /168 kJ per portion. (6 servings)

Add some chopped fresh basil to the sauce if obtainable.

Serves 4-6

900 g /2 lbs firm ripe tomatoes, or 2 x 400 g /14
    oz cans tomatoes, drained
1 tablespoon olive oil
½ teaspoon sugar
1 small garlic clove, finely chopped
salt

Halve the fresh tomatoes and squeeze or spoon out all the seeds. Put the tomato halves or the drained canned tomatoes in a saucepan with the oil, sugar and garlic. Cook over very low heat for 6-7 minutes, stirring frequently.
Transfer the mixture to a sieve and let it drain over a bowl for 10 minutes (use this liquid for soup).
Press the tomatoes through the sieve into the saucepan, then taste the purée and add seasoning. Reheat gently and serve at once with cooked wholemeal pasta.

Serve with: Wholemeal pasta and Parmesan cheese.

rigatoni with ricotta and sage

20 minutes | 645 kcal /2709 kJ per portion as a main course

You could serve this as a starter; this amount would be plenty for 6 people.

Serves 4

450 g /1 lb rigatoni
salt and freshly ground black pepper
1 small onion, finely chopped
1 tablespoon olive oil
250 g /9 oz ricotta cheese
125 ml /4 fl oz milk
4-5 fresh sage leaves, finely chopped

Simmer the rigatoni in a large pan of boiling salted water for 15-20 minutes until cooked but still firm.
Meanwhile, cook the onion in the oil in a small saucepan over low heat for 5 minutes or until clear. Mix the ricotta with milk and sage, add this to the onion and cook for 8 minutes over low heat, stirring continuously. Season with salt and freshly ground pepper.
Drain the rigatoni and place in a large warmed serving dish. Pour the Ricotta sauce over the rigatoni and serve immediately.

Serve with: Green salad.

pasta and tomato soup

chicken liver bake

45 minutes

370 kcal /1554 kJ per portion

The strong flavour of chicken livers means a little will go a long way. This is a main course dish using only 50 g /2 oz liver per person.

Serves 4

225 g /8 oz noodles, wholemeal lasagnetta or spaghetti
225 g /8 oz chicken livers, defrosted if frozen
1 tablespoon oil
1 medium-sized onion, chopped
2 large eggs, beaten
salt and freshly ground black pepper

Heat the oven to 180C/350F/Gas 4. Cook the pasta in a large pan of boiling water until it is tender, about 12 minutes.
Meanwhile, trim and roughly chop the chicken livers. Heat the oil in a frying-pan. Add the onion and cook until it is golden. Push to one side of the pan and add the livers. Fry them until browned and cooked through, about 5 minutes.
Mix together the liver and onion and season with salt and pepper to taste.
Drain the pasta and transfer it to a bowl. Stir in the liver mixture, then the beaten eggs. Check the seasoning.
Transfer the mixture to a 1.1-litre/2-pint pie dish or casserole and bake for about 30 minutes, or until golden. Serve at once.

Serve with: Mixed salad.

pasta and tomato soup

45 minutes

225 kcal /967 kJ per portion

Serves 4

1 tablespoon olive oil
2 cloves garlic, crushed
450 g /1 lb ripe tomatoes, blanched, skinned and coarsely chopped
2 medium-sized onions, thinly sliced
3 tablespoons chopped parsley
1.5-litres /2½-pints water or light stock
salt and freshly ground black pepper
150 g /5 oz wholemeal ditalini, macaroni or other short tubular pasta for soup
25 g /1 oz freshly grated Parmesan cheese

Put the oil in a saucepan over medium heat, add the garlic and sauté until just coloured, about 3-4 minutes. Remove the garlic with a slotted spoon.
Add the chopped tomatoes, onion and half the parsley. Fry gently for 10 minutes, stirring frequently.
Tip this into a large saucepan with the water or stock. Season generously with salt and freshly ground black pepper, and simmer, covered, for 20 minutes. Raise the heat and drop in the pasta. Cook, covered, for about 10 minutes, stirring occasionally, until the pasta is al dente.
Just before serving, add the remaining parsley and the Parmesan cheese. Mix well, pour into a warmed tureen and serve.

Serve with: Warmed wholemeal rolls.

basil, pine nut and parmesan pasta

10 minutes
+ cooking pasta

350 kcal /1470 kJ per portion

Serve this sauce on any type of ribbon pasta.

Serves 4

100 g /4 oz fresh basil leaves
1 tablespoon olive oil
50 g /2 oz pine nuts
1 clove garlic
15 g /½ oz butter
salt and freshly ground black pepper
1 tablespoon parsley sprigs
75 ml /3 fl oz natural yoghurt
100 g /4 oz freshly grated Parmesan cheese
275 g /10 oz wholemeal pasta, freshly cooked,
   to serve

Discard any discoloured basil leaves. Wash the rest and dry them thoroughly with absorbent paper.
Process the basil leaves, olive oil, pine nuts, garlic, butter, salt, parsley and yoghurt in a blender or food processor until the mixture is very creamy. Fold in the Parmesan, season to taste and mix thoroughly.
To serve: add the sauce to the freshly cooked pasta with 3-4 tablespoons of the pasta cooking water. Mix and serve at once.

pasta with pork and orange

pasta with pork and orange

30 minutes

465 kcal /1953 kJ per portion

If you like a rich brown colour sauce, add a few drops of gravy browning to this one.

Serves 4

225 g /8 oz pork sausagemeat
1 tablespoon olive oil
1 small onion, finely chopped
1 orange
150 ml /5 fl oz dry white wine
salt and freshly ground black pepper
225 g /8 oz wholemeal pasta twists
225 g /8 oz button mushrooms, sliced
1 tablespoon finely chopped parsley

Process the sausagemeat in a food processor fitted with a metal blade until it is really smooth. Alternatively pound it with a pestle. Heat the oil in a saucepan over a low heat and cook the onion, stirring occasionally, until it is soft and beginning to colour. Stir in the sausagemeat and cook, stirring all the time until lightly browned. Grate the rind of half the orange and squeeze the juice from this half. (Cut the other half into slices for garnish.) Add the orange rind and juice to the pan with the wine and seasoning to taste. Simmer very gently for 20 minutes.
While the sauce is simmering, cook the pasta in boiling salted water until *al dente*.
Stir the mushrooms into the sauce, cook for 5 minutes more, then spoon it over the pasta, placed on individual plates. Garnish with the parsley and slices of orange and serve.

long pasta with garlic

long pasta with garlic

20 minutes

445 kcal /1869 kJ per portion

Serves 4

350 g /12 oz linguine, spaghetti or vermicelli
salt
4 tablespoons olive oil
3 cloves garlic, very finely chopped
3 tablespoons chopped parsley
1 dried chilli, crushed

Bring a large saucepan of water to the boil. Add some salt and the pasta, all at once. Do not break long pasta, but ease it in to the water gently, bending it as it becomes soft. Stir thoroughly to prevent the pasta from sticking together. Cover the pan, bring the water back to the boil, then remove the lid. Stir again, then adjust the heat so that the water boils fast without boiling over. Meanwhile, prepare the sauce. Heat the oil in a large frying-pan or a large shallow saucepan over medium heat, add the garlic, parsley and chilli and cook for 2 minutes, stirring constantly.
Test the pasta and drain it as soon as it is *al dente*. Strain it in a colander, but be careful not to overdrain or it will become too dry. Add the pasta to the frying-pan and cook it over medium heat for 2 minutes, stirring continually. Serve at once.

pirates' spaghetti

pirates' spaghetti

40 minutes

600 kcal /2520 kJ per portion

If you have difficulty in obtaining clams or squid, substitute shelled cockles or mussels. This would serve 8 people as a starter. See page 31 — seafood salad, for how to prepare fresh squid.

Serves 4

100 g /4 oz small squid
100 g /4 oz shelled small clams
3 cloves garlic, crushed
1 tablespoon oil
100 g /4 oz shrimps
450 g /1 lb wholemeal spaghetti
50 g /2 oz canned anchovy fillets, drained
400 g /14 oz canned peeled tomatoes
salt and freshly ground black pepper
2 tablespoons parsley, finely chopped
1 tablespoon fresh basil, finely chopped

Slice the prepared squid into 2.5-cm/1-inch rounds. Cook the garlic in 1 teaspoon of the oil in a saucepan. When golden, add the clams, squid and shrimps and cook over low heat for 10 minutes.

Simmer the spaghetti in a large pan of boiling salted water for 12-14 minutes until cooked, but still firm when tested. Meanwhile, add the anchovies, tomatoes and salt and pepper to the seafood and continue cooking for 10 minutes.

Drain the spaghetti. Place in a large warmed serving dish and toss in the remaining oil. Pour the sauce on to the pasta and mix again. Sprinkle with parsley and basil and serve immediately.

spaghetti with courgette sauce

35 minutes

505 kcal /2121 kJ per portion

Serves 4

2 tablespoons oil
2 medium-sized onions, finely chopped
1 clove garlic, finely chopped
1 green pepper, thinly sliced
450 g /1 lb courgettes, trimmed and cut into
   5-mm /¼-inch slices
350 g /12 oz tomatoes, blanched, skinned,
   seeded and sliced
1 teaspoon dried oregano
salt and freshly ground black pepper
350 g /12 oz wholemeal spaghetti
50 g /2 oz Parmesan cheese, to serve

spaghetti with courgette sauce

baked macaroni with sardines

1 hour

630 kcal /2646 kJ per portion

Serves 4

350 g /12 oz sardines, fresh or defrosted, if
   frozen
250 g /9 oz fennel bulbs, thinly sliced
2 tablespoons olive oil
1 medium-sized onion, finely chopped
4 anchovy fillets, chopped
50 g /2 oz sultanas
25 g /1 oz pine nuts
1 sachet of saffron powder (optional)
   dissolved in 2 tablespoons warm water
salt and freshly ground black pepper
350 g /12 oz wholemeal bucatini or spaghetti
2 tablespoons dry breadcrumbs

Remove the heads and tails from the sardines. Open the fish out flat by pressing down on their backs with a thumb, then turn them over and remove their backbones. Wash the fish and dry well.

Drop the fennel in a small saucepan of boiling salted water and boil for 10 minutes. Drain, reserving the cooking water, and cut the fennel into very thin, short strips.
Heat the oil in a large frying-pan over low heat. Add the onion and sauté until soft and golden. Add the fennel and sardines and cook for 10 minutes, adding a few tablespoons of the reserved cooking liquid. Meanwhile, mash the anchovies and reserve them.
Heat the oven to 200C/400F/Gas 6. Lift out half the sardines from the pan and reserve them. Add the sultanas, pine nuts, the saffron water if using, and salt and pepper to the sardine mixture remaining in the pan. Cook for a further 5 minutes, stirring. Stir in the anchovies, remove from the heat and keep warm.
Meanwhile, put the fennel liquid in a large saucepan, adding enough water to make up to approximately 3½ litres/6 pints and bring to the boil. Add the pasta and cook until it is *al dente*. Drain the pasta and toss in the sardine-anchovy sauce until well mixed. Grease a deep oven dish with a little oil. Pour half of the pasta into it, cover with the reserved whole sardines and tip in the remaining pasta. Sprinkle with breadcrumbs and put in the oven for 10-15 minutes. Allow the dish to stand for 5 minutes before serving.

Heat the oil and fry the onions over moderate heat for 3 minutes, stirring occasionally. Add the garlic, green pepper and courgettes, stir well and sauté for 2 minutes. Cover the pan, lower heat and simmer for 10 minutes, stirring occasionally.
Add the tomatoes, oregano, salt and pepper and cook, uncovered, over moderate heat for a further 10 minutes. Taste and season if necessary. While the sauce is cooking, cook the spaghetti in a large pan of boiling, salted water for 12-13 minutes, or until just tender. Drain the spaghetti and place in a serving bowl. Spoon the sauce on top. Serve hot with the cheese sprinkled on top.

lemon and lime barley water

lemon and lime barley water

20 minutes + cooling

75 kcal /315 kJ per portion

This refreshing drink tastes even better for the knowledge that it has only natural ingredients.

Serves 4

100 g /4 oz pearl barley
thinly pared rind and juice from 1 small lemon and 1 small lime
50 g /2 oz sugar
1.25 litres /2 pints boiling water

Put the barley into a heavy-based saucepan and cover with cold water. Bring to the boil, then lower the heat and simmer for 10 minutes. Strain off the liquid. Rinse the barley under cold running water and drain.
Put the barley into a large heat-proof jug together with lemon and lime rind and the sugar. Pour over the boiling water, cover and leave for 1-1½ hours, until cold.
Uncover and stir in the lemon and lime juice. Strain the liquid into a clean jug and discard the barley.
Serve the barley water at once or cover and refrigerate. Use within 2 days.

leek and oatmeal soup

55 minutes

131 kcal /550 kJ per portion

Serves 6

6 large leeks
15 g /½ oz butter
700 ml /1¼ pints skimmed milk
700 ml /1¼ pints chicken stock
2 tablespoons oatmeal flakes
salt and freshly ground black pepper
2 tablespoons chopped parsley
50 ml /2 fl oz single cream, to serve

Wash the leeks thoroughly to remove the grit. Use most of the green top for this dish, but trim it neatly. Cut the leeks into chunks about 2.5-cm/1-inch long and wash again if necessary.

Place the butter, milk and stock in a large saucepan over medium heat. When the mixture boils, add the oatmeal, boil for 5 minutes, and then add the chopped leeks. Season with salt and pepper. Cover the pan, lower the heat and simmer gently for 40 minutes.

Add half the parsley and continue cooking for 5 minutes. Serve the soup in warmed bowls with the remaining parsley sprinkled on top and a spoonful of cream swirled on top of each one.

Serve with: Crusty bread.

barley and bacon hotpot

1½ hours

480 kcal /2016 kJ per portion

Serves 4

250 g /9 oz streaky bacon, rinded and finely chopped
2 large onions, thinly sliced
250 g /9 oz carrots, thinly sliced
175 g /6 oz celery, chopped
100 g /4 oz mushrooms, thinly sliced
250 g /9 oz pearl barley
600 ml /1 pint chicken stock
4 tablespoons chopped fresh parsley
salt and freshly ground black pepper

Heat the oven to 180C/350F/Gas 4.
Put the bacon and onions into a flameproof casserole and fry over a medium heat for 5 minutes until the onions are soft and lightly coloured.
Stir in the carrots, celery, mushrooms and pearl barley, then pour in the stock and bring to the boil. Add the parsley and salt and pepper to taste.
Cover the casserole and cook in the oven for 1 hour, or until the barley is soft and nearly all the liquid has been absorbed. Serve hot.

Serve with: Baked potatoes for a really hearty meal.

leek and oatmeal soup

minnesota wild rice

1½ hours

210 kcal /882 kJ per portion

Wild rice is very expensive (and only available in high-class grocers) so it is more usual to combine it with brown rice, as in this recipe.

Serves 4

100 g /4 oz wild rice
100 g /4 oz long-grain brown rice
1 large onion, chopped
150 g /5 oz celery, finely chopped
1.25 litres /2 pints chicken stock
salt and freshly ground black pepper

Heat the oven to 190C/375F/Gas 5. Mix all the ingredients together in a large bowl, then transfer them to a greased 2.3-litre/4-pint ovenproof casserole.
Cover with foil or a lid and bake until the rice is just tender but not split open, and the liquid is absorbed. This will take about 1¼ hours. Serve at once.

Serve with: Any meat dish.

paella

paella

45 minutes   *610 kcal /2562 kJ per portion*

This is a variation on the classical Spanish dish. Serve it to the family or when you have guests, particularly if you have a traditional paella pan.

Serves 4

pinch of saffron
1 large onion, chopped
50 g /2 oz streaky bacon, rinded and chopped
250 g /9 oz long-grain brown rice
2 cloves garlic, crushed
4 chicken thighs, cooked and skinned
200 g /7 oz canned pink salmon, drained and
    flaked
200 g /7 oz canned prawns, drained and
    rinsed
150 g /5 oz canned mussels, drained and
    rinsed
50 g /2 oz frozen peas
300 ml /½ pint chicken stock
salt and freshly ground black pepper

Soak the saffron in 2 tablespoons boiling water.
Fry the chopped bacon and onion in a large frying-pan over low heat until the bacon is cooked and the onion is soft. Add the rice and garlic, mix well and fry for 2 minutes, stirring.
Add the chicken, salmon, prawns, mussels and peas to the pan, spreading the ingredients out evenly over the rice. Pour over the stock and the saffron liquid. Bring to the boil, then lower the heat and simmer for about 20 minutes, stirring occasionally to prevent sticking.
Towards the end of the cooking time, taste the paella and adjust the seasoning if necessary. When it is cooked all the liquid should be absorbed and the rice fluffy. Serve in the cooking pan.

Serve with: Garlic bread and a green salad.

risotto with spring vegetables

0·00	
1 hour	370 kcal /1554 kJ per portion

Special risotto rice is sold in Italian delicatessens; it can absorb a large quantity of liquid without becoming soft or sticky.

Serves 4

1.25 litres /2 pints chicken stock
1 medium-sized onion, finely chopped
1 tablespoon oil
250 g /9 oz rice, preferably Italian
1 medium-sized carrot, finely diced
2 celery stalks, finely diced
100 g /4 oz shelled peas, or defrosted frozen petits pois
100 g /4 oz French beans, cut to 15-mm/½-inch pieces
1 medium-sized courgette, finely diced
2 ripe tomatoes, blanched, skinned, seeds and juices removed, and the flesh diced
75 g /3 oz Parmesan cheese, freshly grated
salt and freshly ground black pepper

Bring the stock to simmering point in a saucepan. Meanwhile, sauté the onion in the oil in a large heavy-based saucepan over a low heat until the onion is soft.

Stir the rice into the onion for 1 minute, then add 200 ml /7 fl oz of the stock and stir constantly with a wooden spoon, loosening the rice from the sides and bottom of the pan. When the stock has been absorbed, stir in another 150 ml /5 fl oz of stock and cook the rice for 10 minutes, stirring constantly. Add the carrot, celery, shelled fresh peas, if using, and French beans. Still stirring, add 150 ml /5 fl oz of simmering stock when the liquid has been absorbed again.

After another 10 minutes, add the courgette, the diced tomato flesh and, if using, the defrosted frozen peas. Continue to cook, stirring and adding stock as necessary. When the rice has absorbed all the stock (this will take about 30 minutes), remove the pan from the heat, add half the Parmesan cheese and check the seasoning.

Cover the pan for 2 minutes, then mix well and turn the risotto into a warmed serving dish. Serve with the rest of the Parmesan.

lamb couscous

lamb couscous

0·00	
2½ hours + overnight soaking	590 kcal /2478 kJ per portion

This is a traditional dish from North Africa. Couscous is available in health food shops.

Serves 6

450 g /1 lb medium or fine couscous
salt
1 tablespoon oil
900 g /2 lbs lean lamb, trimmed of fat and cut into large cubes
1 medium-sized onion, quartered
1 teaspoon chilli powder
1 teaspoon turmeric
450 g /1 lb tomatoes, blanched, skinned, seeded and chopped (or canned, chopped tomatoes)
25 g /1 oz chick-peas, soaked overnight
1 large carrot, scrubbed and cut into 6 strips lengthways
1 large courgette
2-3 small potatoes

Put the couscous into a large bowl. Cover it with cold water and strain immediately through a sieve, shaking to get rid of as much water as possible. Turn the couscous on to a large platter, spreading it out with a fork to break down any lumps.

Fill the bottom pan of a large steamer with water and bring it to the boil. Fit the steamer into place, making sure the steam does not escape from the sides and the water does not touch the bottom of the steamer. Put a layer of couscous in the top of the steamer. When the steam rises, add the rest of the couscous and salt to taste and cook, uncovered for about 30 minutes.

Remove the steamer from the heat and sprinkle about 350 ml /12 fl oz cold water over the couscous. Drain and turn on to a platter.

Place the bottom saucepan of a large steamer over medium-high heat. Heat the oil and fry the cubed meat and onion for about 30 minutes, stirring from time to time. Reduce the heat to medium-low if the meat starts to stick.

Mix the chilli powder and turmeric with the seeded, chopped tomatoes. Add this, the drained chick-peas and 225 ml /8 fl oz fresh water to the meat and onions. Bring the mixture to the boil, lower the heat and simmer for about 1 hour or until the liquid has reduced and the flavours are blended. Add the carrot pieces, the whole courgette and potatoes to the pan with enough water just to cover. Bring to the boil, then simmer for 20-30 minutes.

Meanwhile, put the half-steamed couscous in the top part of the steamer and fit the steamer into place. Steam the couscous, uncovered, in this way for about 20 minutes, fluffing it up occasionally with a fork.

Turn the couscous into a heated serving dish. Spoon off all the surface oil from the stew and serve it separately or piled up in the centre of the couscous.

Serve with: A green salad.

parsley and bulgur salad

Then add the oil to taste, a little at a time. Chop the tomatoes and stir in or reserve them sliced for garnish. Serve the salad on a bed of vine or cos lettuce leaves.

Serve with: Warmed pitta bread.

brown rice supper dish

55 minutes

605 kcal /2541 kJ per portion

A filling and nutritious vegetarian main course.

Serves 4

250 g /9 oz brown rice
1 teaspoon salt
1 tablespoon oil
1 large onion, peeled and chopped
2 celery stalks, finely chopped
1 bunch spring onions washed, trimmed and chopped
1 red-skinned eating apple, cored and chopped
50 g /2 oz raisins
50 g /2 oz flaked almonds
50 g /2 oz roasted peanuts

For the sauce:
2 tablespoons oil
25 g /1 oz flour
300 ml /½ pint skimmed milk
1 tablespoon mild, wholegrain mustard
75 g /3 oz strongly-flavoured Cheddar cheese

Put the rice, 600 ml/1 pint water and salt in a heavy-based saucepan and bring to the boil. Stir once, cover and cook over a low heat for 40-50 minutes, or until the rice is tender and all the water has been absorbed.
While the rice is cooking, make the sauce. Heat the oil in a medium-sized saucepan and stir in the flour. Cook for a minute or two, then add the milk. Stir over a moderate heat, until the mixture thickens, then let the sauce simmer gently for 5-10 minutes to cook the flour. Stir in the mustard and cheese and season to taste. Leave on one side.
Heat the oil in a frying-pan and fry the onion and celery in the oil for 8-10 minutes, taking care not to let them brown. Add the spring onions and cook for 2 minutes more.
Using a fork mix the vegetables with the cooked rice and stir in the apple, raisins, almonds and peanuts. Heap the mixture on a warm serving dish; keep warm for a few minutes whilst reheating the sauce and serve them together.

Serve with: Cooked spinach.

parsley and bulgur salad

15 minutes
+ 15 minutes
soaking

95 kcal /399 kJ per portion

This is a speciality from the Middle East where it is known as Tabbouleh. Serve it as a starter. Bulgur is cracked wheat.

Serves 6

300 g /11 oz flat-leaved parsley
75 g /3 oz fine bulgur
salt and freshly ground black pepper
juice of 1½-2 lemons
4-6 sprigs of mint, finely chopped
4-5 spring onions, finely chopped
1 small onion, finely chopped
2 tablespoons oil
2-3 large tomatoes, blanched, skinned, seeded and drained
very young fresh vine leaves or cos lettuce leaves to serve (optional)

Wash the parsley and remove the stalks. Dry it well and chop it finely. Soak the bulgur in cold water for 10 minutes, rinse and drain well. Sprinkle it with ¼ teaspoon salt and the juice of ½ lemon and leave to soften for at least an hour.
To assemble the salad, first mix together the mint, onions and parsley in a large mixing bowl. Stir in the bulgur, 1 tablespoon at a time so the parsley is evenly distributed. Season with salt, pepper and lemon juice.

cauliflower, mushroom and oat casserole

1 hour

385 kcal /1617 kJ per portion

This tasty unusual casserole is easy to make and filling.

Serves 4

1 medium-sized cauliflower, broken into even-sized florets
salt and freshly ground black pepper
2 tablespoons flour
300 ml /½ pint natural yoghurt
1 teaspoon mild mustard
100 g /4 oz matured Cheddar cheese, grated
225 g /8 oz button mushrooms, trimmed
100 g /4 oz rolled oats
50 g /2 oz coarsely chopped walnuts

Heat the oven to 200C/400F/Gas 6. Drop the cauliflower florets into a saucepan containing 2.5 cm/1 inch boiling, salted water and cook for about 7 minutes, or until they are just tender; drain well and set aside. Meanwhile, put the flour into a small bowl and blend to a smooth paste with a little of the yoghurt. Gradually stir in the remaining yoghurt, the mustard, half the grated cheese and salt and freshly ground black pepper to taste.
Fold the cauliflower and mushrooms into the yoghurt mixture, turning gently so that all the vegetables are coated. Pour into a shallow ovenproof dish.
Using a fork, mix the remaining cheese with the oats, then add the walnuts to make a lumpy, crumbly mixture. Sprinkle evenly over the cauliflower and mushrooms and bake for 20 minutes or until the topping is golden brown and crisp. Serve at once.

wheaty pea and vegetable salad

wheaty pea and vegetable salad

2¼ hours
+ overnight
soaking

345 kcal /1449 kJ per
portion

This is an unusual salad which is tasty and filling.

Serves 4

100 g /4 oz whole wheat grains
100 g /4 oz green or yellow split peas
2 tablespoons olive oil
1 tablespoon red wine vinegar
salt and freshly ground black pepper
2 medium-sized carrots, grated
2 celery stalks, chopped
5-cm /2-inch piece of cucumber, chopped
4 spring onions, chopped
2 medium-sized tomatoes, blanched, skinned
    and chopped
4 lettuce leaves, shredded
25 g /1 oz raisins
a little cress, to garnish

For the dressing:
175 g /6 oz curd cheese
50 ml /2 fl oz milk

Cover the whole wheat grains with cold water and leave to soak overnight. Next day, cook the wheat in plenty of water for 1¼-1½ hours, or until the grains are tender and beginning to burst. Drain and cool slightly. Meanwhile, put the split peas into a saucepan filled with cold water and simmer for about 25 minutes, until just tender but still whole. Drain.
Put the oil, vinegar, salt and pepper into a large bowl and mix together, then add the wheat and peas. Let cool completely.
Stir in the carrots, celery, cucumber, spring onions, tomatoes, lettuce and raisins, tossing gently until well coated with the oil and vinegar mixture. Divide between 4 bowls.
To make the dressing, beat together the curd cheese and milk until smooth. Put a large spoonful of dressing on top of each bowl and sprinkle with a little cress.

spiced almond beef

2¾ hours

500 kcal /2100 kJ per portion

Serves 4

700 g /1½ lbs chuck steak
1 tablespoon oil
1 medium-sized onion, chopped
3 celery stalks, chopped
2 teaspoons mild curry powder
dash of Tabasco, or 1 teaspoon
    Worcestershire sauce
25 g /1 oz almonds
40 g /1½ oz ground almonds
40 g /1½ oz plain flour
425 ml /15 fl oz beef stock
185 g /6½ oz can pimientos, drained and sliced
salt

To garnish:
25 g /1 oz flaked almonds
celery leaves

Heat the oven to 170C/325F/Gas 3. Trim off any fat from the steak and cut into 2.5-cm/1-inch cubes.
Heat the oil in a large saucepan. Add the beef cubes and fry over a brisk heat for 2-3 minutes, stirring occasionally, to seal and brown. Using a slotted spoon, transfer the beef cubes to a casserole.
Add the onion and celery to the frying-pan and fry gently for 2 minutes. Stir in the curry powder, Tabasco, almonds and ground almonds. Sprinkle in the flour and gradually stir in the stock, then add the pimientos. Bring to the boil, lower the heat and simmer for a few minutes. Season with salt and pour over the beef. Stir lightly.
Cover the casserole and cook in the lowest part of the oven for 2-2½ hours until the beef is cooked through and tender when pierced with a sharp knife.
Sprinkle with toasted almonds, garnish with celery leaves and serve hot, straight from the dish.

Serve with: Baked potatoes.

almond pilaff

1¼ hours

340 kcal /1428 kJ per portion

Serves 4

50 g /2 oz almonds
15 g /½ oz butter
1 medium-sized onion, thinly sliced
225 g /8 oz long-grain brown rice
1 teaspoon ground turmeric
1 teaspoon ground cumin
600 ml /1 pint stock
a pinch of sea salt
50 g /2 oz raisins

Heat the oven to 180C/350F/Gas 4. Blanch and split the almonds. Melt the butter in a flameproof casserole on a high heat. Add the almonds and stir to brown them evenly. Remove them with a slotted spoon and put on one side.
Lower the heat and add the onion. Cook for about 5 minutes to soften then stir in the rice, turmeric and cumin and cook for 1½ minutes. Pour in the stock and bring it to the boil. Season.
Cover the casserole and cook in the oven for 45 minutes. Remove from the oven and mix in the almonds and raisins. Cover the casserole again and let it stand for 10 minutes before serving.

Serve with: Chicken, pork or lamb or as part of a vegetarian meal.

carrot and nut roast

1¼ hours

570 kcal /2394 kJ per portion

Serves 4

100 g /4 oz cashew nuts or pieces
200 g /7 oz walnut pieces
100 g /4 oz wholemeal bread
2 tablespoons oil
1 medium-sized onion, finely chopped
225 g /8 oz carrots, coarsely grated
6 tablespoons vegetable stock
2 tablespoons yeast extract
1 teaspoon honey
1 teaspoon dried mixed herbs
2 teaspoons lemon juice
salt and freshly ground black pepper

Heat the oven to 180C/350F/Gas 4. Grease a shallow ovenproof dish. Grind the cashews, walnuts and bread together in batches in a blender until the mixture is fairly fine. Tip into a bowl.
Heat the oil in a saucepan, add the onion and fry gently for 5 minutes until soft and lightly coloured. Add the carrots and cook, stirring, for a further 5 minutes. Remove from the pan with a slotted spoon and add to the nuts and bread in the bowl. Put the stock in a bowl, add the yeast extract and honey and stir until the honey has dissolved. Stir into the nut mixture with the herbs and lemon juice. Taste the mixture and season with salt and pepper. Spoon the mixture into prepared dish and bake in the oven for 45 minutes. Serve hot or cold.

Serve with: Salad and boiled potatoes if hot; French bread if cold.

carrot and nut roast

nutty rissoles

*1 hour
+ chilling*

*600 kcal /2520 kJ per
portion*

*A satisfying vegetarian dish that is delicious
with home-made tomato sauce (see
page 61).*

Serves 4

225 g /8 oz mixed nuts, finely chopped
25 g /1 oz butter
1 large onion, finely chopped
1 large clove garlic, crushed
175 g /6 oz button mushrooms, finely
    chopped
100 g /4 oz fresh wholemeal breadcrumbs
1 tablespoon chopped parsley
2 teaspoons dried mixed herbs
2 tablespoons tomato purée
1 teaspoon soy sauce
1 egg, beaten
salt and freshly ground black pepper
3 tablespoons plain flour
2 tablespoons oil
mushroom slices and walnut halves, to
    garnish

Melt the butter in a frying-pan and fry the
onions and garlic over a low heat for about 5
minutes – until soft. Remove from the heat
and stir in the nuts, mushrooms,
breadcrumbs, parsley and mixed herbs.
Blend everything together well.
Add the tomato purée and soy sauce and
sufficient beaten egg to bind the mixture
together. Season to taste with salt and
pepper.
Roll heaped tablespoons of the mixture in
flour to form 12 balls. Flatten these into
rissoles about 7.5 cm/3 inches in diameter.
Place on a floured baking sheet and chill for 1
hour.
Heat 1 tablespoon oil in a large frying-pan
and fry 6 of the rissoles in a single layer,
cooking them for 3-5 minutes on each side,
until crisp and golden. Drain on absorbent
paper while you cook the remaining rissoles
in the rest of the oil. Serve hot, garnished
with mushroom slices and the walnut halves.

Serve with: Homemade tomato sauce and
mashed potatoes.

courgettes with onion and nuts

courgettes with onion and nuts

20 minutes

*135 kcal /567 kJ per
portion*

*Almonds or walnuts could be used instead of
pine nuts.*

Serves 4

450 g /1 lb courgettes
25 g /1 oz butter
3 tablespoons water
salt and freshly ground black pepper
1 medium-sized onion, sliced into rings
25 g /1 oz pine nuts

Cut the courgettes into quarters lengthways,
then cut across to make even-sized sticks.
Melt half the butter in a saucepan with the
water and a pinch of salt. Add the
courgettes, cover the pan and cook gently
for 10 minutes until the courgettes are just
tender. Shake the pan occasionally during
this time to ensure that they cook evenly.
Meanwhile, melt the remaining butter in a
frying-pan, add the onion rings and fry
briskly for 3 minutes until lightly browned.
Transfer with a slotted spoon to a plate and
set aside. Add the pine nuts to the pan and
fry for 2 minutes, stirring, until golden
brown.
Drain the courgettes, season to taste with
salt and pepper, and transfer them to a
warmed shallow serving dish. Arrange the
onion rings down the centre of the
courgettes and sprinkle the pine nuts over
the top.

Serve with: Plain grilled meat or fish.

hazelnut steaks

45 minutes | **470 kcal /1974 kJ per portion**

A delicious mixture of textures; the crunchy hazelnuts are a perfect foil for the steak.

Serves 4

4 pieces frying steak, each weighing about
    175 g /6 oz
2 tablespoons oil
75 g /3 oz skinned hazelnuts, chopped
1 small bunch spring onions, chopped
25 g /1 oz fresh wholemeal breadcrumbs
finely grated rind of 1 small orange
salt and freshly ground black pepper
1 teaspoon Demerara sugar
orange twists, to garnish

Trim off any fat from the steak.
Heat half the oil in a frying-pan and add
50 g/2 oz hazelnuts and the spring onions.
Fry gently for 5 minutes until the onions are
soft and very lightly coloured. Transfer to a
bowl and stir in breadcrumbs, orange rind
and salt and pepper to taste.
Put the remaining hazelnuts in a saucepan
and shake over moderate heat, until the nuts
are golden brown on all sides. Remove from
the pan and place on absorbent paper to cool
while cooking the steaks.
Place the steaks between 2 pieces of
greaseproof paper. Using a meat mallet or
rolling pin, beat each steak out to a rectangle
measuring about 12.5 x 7.5 cm /5 x 3 inches.
Remove the greaseproof paper. Spoon one
quarter of the onion and hazelnut mixture on
to one half of each steak, spreading it to
within 15mm /½ inch of the edges. Fold over
the other half of the steak and secure each of
the open edges with wooden cocktail sticks.
Heat the remaining oil in the frying-pan. Add
the sugar and stir until dissolved, then add
the steaks and fry for 7-10 minutes on each
side, until browned and cooked through.
Transfer the cooked steaks to a warmed
serving dish and remove the wooden cocktail
sticks.
Sprinkle over the cooked browned hazelnuts,
garnish with orange twists and serve at once.

Serve with: Boiled potatoes and any green
vegetables in season.

hazelnut steaks

kidney and chestnut sauté

kidney and chestnut sauté

30 minutes | *385 kcal/1617 kJ per portion*

Serves 4

750 g /1½ lb lamb kidneys, halved lengthways, skinned and cored
1 tablespoon oil
1 bunch spring onions, chopped
440 g /15½ oz can whole chestnuts in water, drained and cut into small pieces
2 teaspoons French mustard
150 ml /5 fl oz natural yoghurt
1 tablespoon snipped chives or chopped parsley
salt and freshly ground black pepper

Cut each kidney half into 2-3 even-sized pieces if they are large.
Heat the oil in a frying-pan, add the spring onions and fry gently for about 5 minutes until soft. Add the kidneys to the pan and fry gently, stirring frequently, for about 5 minutes, until the kidneys have lost all their pinkness.
Add the chestnuts to the pan and stir over gentle heat until heated through.
Add the mustard and yoghurt and continue stirring until the mixture is heated through. Do not allow to boil. Remove from the heat, stir in the chives and season to taste with salt and pepper. Transfer to a warmed dish and serve.

Serve with: Boiled rice and a green salad or boiled carrots.

walnut, apricot and bean salad

walnut, apricot and bean salad

30 minutes
+ soaking +
chilling

195 kcal /819 kJ per
portion

An unusual salad; you will probably have the ingredients ready to hand in the larder and freezer.

Serves 4

75 g /3 oz dried apricots
1 teaspoon grated orange rind
450 g /1 lb frozen runner beans
200 g /7 oz can sweetcorn, drained
50 g /2 oz walnut halves

For the dressing:
1 tablespoon orange juice
1 tablespoon olive oil
1 teaspoon clear honey
few drops lemon juice
salt and freshly ground pepper

Cover the apricots with cold water and leave to stand for 3 hours. Put the apricots into a saucepan with their soaking water and bring to the boil. Cover, lower the heat and simmer for 5-10 minutes, until the apricots are just soft. Drain, cut into strips and mix with the orange rind in a salad bowl.
Cook the beans as instructed on the packet giving them the minimum cooking time. Drain and rinse under cold water. Drain well again and add to the apricots with the sweetcorn.
Chop half the walnuts roughly and add them to the salad. Toss everything together.
Make the dressing by whisking together all the ingredients. Pour over the salad, cover with cling film and chill for at least 30 minutes. Just before serving, arrange the remaining walnut halves over the salad.

Serve with: Cold meats or with garlic bread as a starter.

nutty potato layer

1 hour

405 kcal /1701 kJ per
portion

The nuts, cheese and potato in this dish make it a well-balanced meal in itself. It is an ideal way of using left-over cheese.

Serves 4

900 g /2 lbs potatoes, peeled and cubed
salt and freshly ground white pepper
25 g /1 oz margarine
2 medium-sized onions, sliced
3 tablespoons skimmed milk
pinch of grated nutmeg
75 g /3 oz hard cheese, grated
50 g /2 oz salted peanuts, roughly chopped
1 tablespoon chopped parsley

Heat the oven to 200C/400F/Gas 6. Cook the potatoes in boiling salted water until just tender – about 10 minutes.
Meanwhile, melt the margarine in a saucepan and fry the onions over a moderate heat until they are soft and lightly coloured – about 5 minutes. Drain on absorbent paper.
Drain the potatoes and mash with the milk, nutmeg and salt and pepper to taste. Spread a third of this over the base of a 1.25-litre/2-pint ovenproof dish. Cover with half the onions and half the cheese.
Repeat these layers once more and then top with the remaining potato, smoothing the surface with a fork.
Sprinkle the nuts over the potato and bake in the oven for 25-30 minutes, until golden. Sprinkle with parsley and serve at once.

hazelnut and red cabbage salad

15 minutes

200 kcal /840 kJ per
portion

Serves 4

225 g /8 oz red cabbage, shredded
75 g /3 oz stoned dates, chopped
50 g /2 oz shelled hazelnuts, roughly chopped
2 celery stalks, thinly sliced
2 dessert apples, cored and sliced
1 orange, thinly sliced, to garnish

For the dressing:
2 tablespoons oil
2 tablespoons orange juice
1 teaspoon finely grated orange rind
salt and freshly ground pepper

Make the dressing by mixing together all the ingredients very thoroughly. Mix together the shredded cabbage, dates, hazelnuts and sliced celery and place in a salad bowl.
Prepare the apples and drop them straight into the dressing. Tip into the salad bowl, and toss the vegetables to mix them and distribute the dressing evenly.
Garnish with orange slices and serve.

Serve with: Cold meats, particularly poultry, or as a first course piled onto lettuce leaves and served with warmed French bread.

tomato and egg bakes

tomato and egg bakes

20 minutes

100 kcal /420 kJ per portion

This would be lovely for a leisurely breakfast.

Serves 4

4 tomatoes, skinned
1 teaspoon chopped fresh basil, or ½ teaspoon dried basil
salt and freshly ground black pepper
4 large eggs
basil leaves, to garnish

Heat the oven to 180C/350F/Gas 4. Dice the tomatoes and divide between four 150 ml/5 fl oz individual ovenproof dishes or ramekins. Sprinkle a little of the basil into each dish and season with salt and pepper. Mix well. Break 1 egg into each dish on top of the mixture. Cover with foil. Place the dishes on a baking sheet and bake in the oven for 10-12 minutes until the white is set but the yolks are still runny. Serve at once.

Serve with: Wholemeal rolls warmed in the oven.

curried eggs with biriani rice

50 minutes

495 kcal /2079 kJ per portion

If you use brown rice in this dish, it will provide a high-fibre meal.

Serves 4

8 eggs
1 tablespoon vegetable oil
1 medium-sized onion, peeled and finely chopped
1 clove garlic, peeled and crushed
1 tablespoon ground coriander
1 teaspoon ground cumin
½ teaspoon chilli powder
salt
4 large tomatoes, blanched, skinned and chopped
600 ml/1 pint chicken stock, make with a cube

For the biriani rice:
2 tablespoons oil
225 g /8 oz basmati, patna or long-grain brown rice, rinsed and drained
1 teaspoon ground cumin
½ teaspoon ground turmeric
salt and freshly ground black pepper
700 ml /1¼ pints hot chicken stock
225 g /8 oz frozen mixed vegetables

Cook the eggs in boiling water for 8 minutes. Meanwhile, heat the oil in a large heavy pan or flameproof casserole. Add the onion, garlic, spices and salt to taste and fry gently for 5 minutes until the onion is soft, stirring constantly.
Add the chopped tomatoes to the pan and stir-fry for a few minutes. Stir in the stock and bring to the boil. Lower the heat and simmer uncovered for 20 minutes, stirring occasionally.
Prepare the rice: heat the oil in a heavy pan, add the rice, spices and salt to taste and fry gently for 5 minutes, stirring constantly. Pour in the hot stock and the frozen vegetables. Stir once, then cover and cook over gentle heat for 20 minutes until the rice is tender. Shell the hard-boiled eggs and add to the curry sauce. Cook for a further 20 minutes, spooning the sauce over the eggs from time to time so they become well coated.

When the rice is tender, add salt and pepper to taste. Arrange the rice around the edge of a warmed serving dish. Taste and adjust the seasoning of the sauce; pour into the centre of the rice with the eggs. Serve at once.

Serve with: Natural yoghurt, sliced banana and pickles.

baked spinach omelette

40 minutes

185 kcal /777 kJ per portion

This is an easy way to make an omelette. The marriage of eggs and spinach is quite delicious.

Serves 4

700 g /1½ lbs fresh spinach, washed, stalks and large midribs discarded
salt and freshly ground black pepper
2 tablespoons oil
1 medium-sized onion, finely chopped
4 large eggs, beaten

Heat the oven to 190C/375F/Gas 5. Place the spinach in a large saucepan with only the water that clings to the leaves after washing. Sprinkle with salt, cover and cook over low heat for 5 minutes, shaking the pan constantly.
Meanwhile, heat the oil in a large frying-pan, add the onion and fry gently for 5 minutes until soft.
Drain the spinach very thoroughly and chop it roughly. Add the chopped spinach to the frying-pan and turn to coat in the oil and onion mixture. Remove the pan from the heat.
Season the eggs with salt and pepper, then pour half the eggs into a shallow ovenproof dish. Spread the chopped spinach evenly over the top, then cover with the remaining egg.
Bake in the oven for 15 minutes until the egg is set. Serve hot or cold, cut into wedges.

Serve with: Tomato salad or baked tomatoes.

egg mousse

provençal anchovy omelettes

15 minutes

2

285 kcal/1197 kJ per portion

Serves 4

50 g /2 oz canned anchovy fillets in oil, drained
2 cloves garlic, finely chopped
1 tablespoon finely chopped parsley
few drops of lemon juice
salt and freshly ground black pepper
8 medium-sized eggs
40 g /1½ oz butter

To garnish:
50 g /2 oz canned anchovy fillets in oil, drained
25 g /1 oz black olives, stoned and halved

Place the anchovy fillets and garlic in a mortar or bowl and pound or mash to a smooth paste. Add the parsley and season to taste with a few drops of lemon juice and a little freshly ground black pepper.
Break the eggs into a bowl and beat vigorously with a fork or wire whisk. Add the anchovy mixture, taste and season carefully (do not add too much salt; the anchovies will be salty).
Heat a 15-cm/6-inch heavy-based frying-pan over a moderate heat, add a quarter of the butter, then pour in a quarter of the egg mixture. Cook the omelette, lifting the edges to permit the liquid egg to run underneath and shaking the pan to prevent sticking. Fry until golden on the underside. Slide onto a serving plate and keep warm while you repeat this process to make the remaining 3 omelettes.
Cut the anchovy fillets for garnish in 3, lengthways, and use to make a lattice pattern over each omelette. Add the black olives and serve immediately.

Serve with: Green salad and bread.

egg mousse

40 minutes
+ draining
cucumber and
chilling

2

125 kcal/525 kJ per portion as a starter
190 kcal/798 kJ per portion as a main course

This recipe makes use of one of the low-calorie substitutes — salad cream — for a high-calorie ingredient. The low-calorie content is mainly achieved by reducing the fat.

Serves 6 as a starter, 4 as a main course

225 g /8 oz cucumber, peeled, seeded and
    finely chopped
salt and freshly ground black pepper
3 hard-boiled eggs, finely chopped
2 spring onions, finely chopped
3 tablespoons finely chopped parsley
175 ml /6 fl oz low-calorie salad cream
50 ml /2 fl oz natural yoghurt
1 tablespoon powdered gelatine
3 tablespoons water
1 medium-sized egg white

To garnish:
6-8 anchovy fillets, soaked in milk for 10
    minutes, drained and split lengthways
2 hard-boiled eggs, sliced
slivers of spring onion tops
fresh parsley leaves

Sprinkle the cucumber lightly with salt and toss well; turn into a colander, weigh down with a plate and leave to drain for at least 30 minutes. Remove the plate and press the cucumber gently to extract any remaining liquid from it.
Turn the cucumber into a bowl, add the chopped eggs, spring onions and parsley and mix well.
In a large bowl, blend the salad cream and yoghurt. Sprinkle the gelatine over the water in a small, heavy-based saucepan and leave to soak for 5 minutes; set the pan over a very low heat for 2-3 minutes until the gelatine is completely dissolved. Remove from the heat. Stir a few spoonfuls of the salad cream mixture into the dissolved gelatine then tip this back into the bulk of the mixture in the bowl, stirring continuously. (Use a spatula to scrape out the pan.) Stir in the egg and cucumber mixture and season to taste with black pepper. Chill until just beginning to thicken.
In a clean, dry bowl, whisk the egg white until soft peaks form, and fold this into the egg mousse. Turn the mousse into a serving bowl and chill for 2-3 hours until set. Just before serving, arrange the split anchovies in a lattice over the top of the mousse and place slices of hard-boiled egg around the edge. Garnish with spring onion and parsley, then serve chilled.

Serve with: Crusty bread, and a salad for a main course.

fresh asparagus with egg dressing

35 minutes + cooling | 135 kcal / 567 kJ per portion

If you do not have a narrow enough saucepan to allow the asparagus to stand firmly, place a jam jar filled with hot water in the centre of pan and arrange the asparagus around it.

Serves 4

450 g / 1 lb fresh slender asparagus spears
salt

For the dressing:
2 teaspoons lemon juice
1 tablespoon white wine vinegar
3 tablespoons olive oil
$\frac{1}{4}$ teaspoon salt
freshly ground black pepper
$\frac{1}{4}$ teaspoon mustard powder
1 teaspoon capers, chopped
1 teaspoon finely chopped parsley
1 teaspoon snipped chives
1 hard-boiled egg, finely chopped

Wash the asparagus stalks well in cold water, then trim the tough base from each spear. Make sure the spears are trimmed to an even length, then divide into 4 separate bundles. Tie each bundle securely with string just below the tips and towards the base.
Half-fill a deep narrow saucepan with lightly salted water and bring to the boil. Remove from the heat and stand the bundles of asparagus upright in the pan with the tips extending out of the water so that they cook in steam. Cover the pan with foil to make a domed lid high enough to cover the asparagus without crushing the tips.
Return the pan to the heat, bring to the boil and boil gently for about 20 minutes, or until the thick part of the stem feels tender when pierced with a sharp knife.
Lift out the asparagus very carefully with kitchen tongs, then drain on absorbent paper. Lay on a clean, folded tea-cloth and leave for at least 2 hours until cold. Meanwhile, make the dressing: put all the ingredients in a screw-top jar, replace the lid and shake. Cut the strings around the asparagus, then arrange the cold spears on 4 individual plates and pour over the dressing.

fresh asparagus with egg dressing

cheesy stuffed peppers

cheesy stuffed peppers

`0·00`

55 minutes

270 kcal/1134 kJ per portion

Serves 4

4 red peppers, each weighing about
175 g/6 oz, tops sliced off and seeded
1 tablespoon vegetable oil
1 medium-sized onion, chopped
75 g/3 oz fresh wholemeal breadcrumbs
75 g/3 oz Edam cheese, grated
75 g/3 oz almonds
2 tomatoes, skinned and chopped
1 tablespoon tomato purée
1 teaspoon dried thyme
salt and freshly ground black pepper

Bring a large saucepan of water to the boil,
add the pepper cases and tops and blanch by
boiling for 3 minutes. Drain thoroughly. Heat
the oven to 190C/375F/Gas 5.
Lightly grease a shallow ovenproof dish and
arrange the pepper cases upright in the dish.

Heat the oil in a saucepan, add the onion and
fry gently for 8-10 minutes until lightly
browned. Remove the pan from the heat and
stir in the remaining ingredients with salt and
pepper to taste. Divide the mixture between
the pepper cases and replace the tops.
Bake the peppers, uncovered, in the oven for
about 40 minutes, until the filling is lightly
browned. Serve hot, straight from the dish.

Serve with: Boiled wholewheat noodles and
green salad.

cottage cheese and chive bakes

35 minutes

156 kcal /655 kJ per portion

Cottage cheese flavoured with sweetcorn or chives or pineapple could be used to vary this simple recipe.

Serves 4

175 g /6 oz cottage cheese
4 medium-sized eggs
50 g /2oz cooked ham, chopped
1 tablespoon snipped chives
salt and freshly ground black pepper

Heat the oven to 200C/400F/Gas 6 and lightly grease 4 ramekins. Put all the ingredients into a bowl and mix lightly together with a fork until well combined. Divide the mixture between the ramekins. Bake in the oven for 20-25 minutes until puffed up and golden brown. Serve at once.

Serve with: Grilled tomatoes and green beans.

cheese pâté

15 minutes
+ freezing and standing

125 kcal /525 kJ per portion

This can either be made in one dish or in individual dishes.

Serves 4

175 g /6 oz curd cheese
175 g /6 oz cottage cheese
2 cloves garlic, crushed
1 tablespoon snipped chives
salt and freshly ground black pepper
25 g /1 oz black peppercorns, crushed

Grease a 425-ml/¾-pint straight-sided casserole or soufflé dish with oil.
Put the cheeses into a bowl and beat until

cheese pâté

very soft, then beat in the garlic and chives until well blended. Season with salt and freshly ground black pepper to taste.
Spoon the cheese mixture into the prepared dish and smooth the top. Cover with a lid or foil and freeze for 30 minutes.
Take the pâté from the freezer and remove the lid or foil. Place a small flat serving plate on top of the pâté, then invert and carefully turn the pâté out.
Using a palette knife, press the crushed peppercorns on to the pâté to coat the top and sides completely. Brush away any excess crushed peppercorns and then wipe the plate clean.
Place in the refrigerator for 30 minutes, then stand at room temperature for 15 minutes. Serve with a spoon, to scoop out individual portions.

Serve with: Wholewheat crackers, grapes and a green salad.

cheesecake pots

30 minutes
+ chilling

215 kcal /903 kJ per
portion

Any type of fresh fruit in season could be used to decorate these sweets, but berries look particularly attractive.

Serves 6

1 rounded tablespoon gelatine
3 tablespoons water
350 g /12 oz cottage cheese
50 g /2 oz caster sugar
finely grated rind of 2 oranges
2-3 drops of vanilla essence
1 egg white
75 ml /3 fl oz natural yoghurt

For the base:
25 g /1 oz butter
75 g /3 oz wholemeal bran or digestive
   biscuits, finely crushed

To decorate:
fresh fruit
mint sprigs or leaves (optional)

Cut 6 x 25-cm/10-inch squares of cling film and use to line 6 x 150-ml/5-fl oz ramekin dishes, draping the excess over the sides. Sprinkle the gelatine over the water in a small heatproof bowl. Stand in a pan of very hot water and stir until the gelatine has dissolved. Leave to cool.
Place the cheese, sugar, orange rind and vanilla essence in a blender or food processor and blend until smooth. Pour in the cooled gelatine and blend again.
Pour the cheese mixture into a bowl, cover and chill for 30-40 minutes until thickened but not set. Whisk the egg white until stiff. Fold the yoghurt and then the beaten egg white into the cheese mixture using a metal spoon. Pour into the prepared dishes.
To make the bases, melt the butter in a small saucepan, remove from the heat and stir in the biscuit crumbs. Divide the crumbs evenly between the dishes placing them on top of the cheese mixture. Pack it down firmly. Fold the excess cling film over the top of each dish, then chill for at least 3 hours, until set. A few minutes before serving, uncover the cheesecakes and run a round-bladed knife between the sides of the dish and the cling

film. Turn out the cheesecakes on to a serving plate and peel off the cling film. Decorate the surface of each cheesecake with fruit, and mint (if using).

baked cucumbers with curd cheese

1½ hours
+ degorging
portion

120 kcal /505 kJ per
cucumber

An unusual vegetable dish which will be very economical when cucumbers are in abundance.

Serves 4

2 medium-sized cucumbers, peeled
salt and white pepper
25 g /1 oz butter
1 small onion, sliced
100 g /4 oz curd cheese
4 tablespoons milk
chopped chives to garnish

Cut the cucumbers into 1.5-mm /½-inch chunks, sprinkle with salt and leave to degorge for at least 30 minutes.
Heat the oven to 180C/350F/Gas 4. Melt the butter in a frying-pan and fry the onion until it is soft, but not browned. Rinse and drain the cucumber and add to the pan, stirring so that all the chunks are coated with butter. Remove from the heat and place in a lightly buttered ovenproof dish.
Mix the curd cheese with the milk until it is smooth, and season with white pepper. Spread the cheese mixture over the cucumber, cover and bake for approximately 1 hour, or until the cucumber is just tender, but not soggy. Sprinkle with chopped chives and serve at once.

Serve with: Lean cold meat and baked potatoes.

cheesy castles

20 minutes
+ draining time

210 kcal /882 kJ per
portion

Small yoghurt, cottage cheese or salad cartons will make ideal moulds for these puddings.

Serves 4

cheesy castles

225 g /8 oz cottage cheese
150 ml /5 fl oz soured cream
150 ml /5 fl oz natural yoghurt
3-4 drops vanilla flavouring
1 tablespoon caster sugar
350 g /12 oz black or red cherries

Using a skewer, punch 8 or 9 holes in the base of four 150-ml/5-fl oz moulds. Line each mould with a large square of wet muslin, allowing the excess muslin to hang over the sides of the moulds.

Drain any liquid from the cheese, then press the cheese through a nylon sieve into a bowl. Slowly stir in the cream, yoghurt and vanilla flavouring. Add the sugar and mix well until evenly distributed. Pour the mixture into the prepared moulds. Fold the overhanging pieces of muslin over the cheese mixture to enclose it completely, then lightly press the top down.
Put the moulds on a wire rack, standing on a plate or tray, then refrigerate for at least 12 hours (and up to 24 hours) to drain away excess moisture.

To unmould the castles: remove one of the drained moulds from refrigerator and unwrap the top. Invert a small dessert plate on top of the mould, then turn over the plate and mould together. Lift off the mould and carefully remove the muslin.
Unmould the remaining cheese castles in the same way. Transfer the castles to a serving plate using a fish slice and arrange the cherries around the base of the castles. Serve at once.

savoury yoghurt cheese

10 minutes
+ draining

65 kcal / 275 kJ per
portion

Serves 8

1.25 litres / 2 pints natural yoghurt
1 teaspoon salt
1 teaspoon fresh mint leaves
paprika

Beat the yoghurt with the salt, adding more if
you like, and pour the yoghurt into a
colander lined with a damp muslin or fine
cheesecloth. Tie the corners of the cloth
together and suspend it over the sink to let
the whey drain away overnight.
    Serve the creamy white cheese in a bowl,
garnished with chopped mint and sprinkled
with paprika.

Serve with: Raw vegetable crudités

home-made thickened yoghurt

10 minutes
+ standing +
chilling

356 kcal / 1495 kJ per
600 ml / 1 pint

A basic recipe for thickened yoghurt. If you
prefer runnier yoghurt, do not add as much
dried milk powder.

Makes 600 ml / 1 pint

600 ml / 1 pint skimmed milk
2 tablespoons natural yoghurt
3 tablespoons skimmed milk powder

Warm the milk until almost boiling. Turn off
the heat and leave to cool to 40-43C /
105-110F. (If you do not have a thermometer,
hold your little finger in the milk to the count
of ten – if it still feels hot, the temperature is
right.)
Mix the yoghurt and milk powder together to
a thick paste. Beat in the milk gradually until
thoroughly combined and free from lumps.
Pour into a vacuum flask rinsed out with hot
water and insert the stopper immediately.
Leave undisturbed for 8 hours or until thick.
Transfer to a covered container and chill in
the refrigerator for about 1 hour before
using.

yoghurt and lemon soup

10 minutes
+ chilling

80 kcal / 336 kJ per
portion (6 servings)

Serves 4-6

600 ml / 1 pint natural yoghurt, chilled
600 ml / 1 pint tomato juice, chilled
1 teaspoon tomato purée
½ small cucumber, peeled and finely diced
1 medium-sized green pepper, finely chopped
2 spring onions, thinly sliced
juice and grated rind of 1 large lemon
salt and freshly ground black pepper
large pinch of cayenne pepper
½ teaspoon mild paprika
1 tablespoon chopped chives
thin lemon slices, to garnish
lemon wedges, to serve

Tip the yoghurt into a large bowl and
gradually beat in the tomato juice and purée
until the mixture is smooth and well blended.
Stir in the cucumber, green pepper, spring
onion, lemon juice and rind. Season to taste
with salt and black pepper and stir in the
cayenne and paprika.
Cover and chill until needed. Just before
serving, stir in the chopped chives. Pour the
soup into chilled bowls, garnish with lemon
slices and serve very cold, with a lemon
wedge for each person.

Serve with: Melba toast or pumpernickel.

yoghurt and lemon soup

honey cream

10 minutes   105 kcal /441 kJ per portion

Serve this sweet-tasting cream with any fresh fruit or with an unsweetened fruit salad.

Serves 6

75 g /3 oz curd cheese
2 tablespoons skimmed milk
2 tablespoons clear honey
grated rind of 1 lemon
75 ml /3 fl oz double cream
100 ml /3½ fl oz natural yoghurt

Soften the cheese by beating it with a wooden spoon, then gradually beat in the milk, honey and lemon rind.
Whip the cream with the yoghurt until it is thick, but not really stiff. Gradually whip in the cheese mixture. Cover the bowl with cling film and refrigerate it until you want it.

sweet lassi

10 minutes   115 kcal /483 kJ per portion

Serves 4

4 ice cubes
500 ml /18 fl oz natural yoghurt
300 ml /½ pint ice-cold water
2 tablespoons caster sugar
cumin seeds, crushed (optional)

Put an ice-cube into each of 4 full glass tumblers. Put half the yoghurt into the goblet of a blender with half the water and 1 tablespoon sugar. Blend for 20-30 seconds until frothy, then pour into 2 of the tumblers. Make two more drinks with the remaining yoghurt, water and sugar in the same way. Pour into the remaining glasses.
Sprinkle crushed cumin on top of each drink, if liked. Serve at once while the drinks are still cold and very frothy.

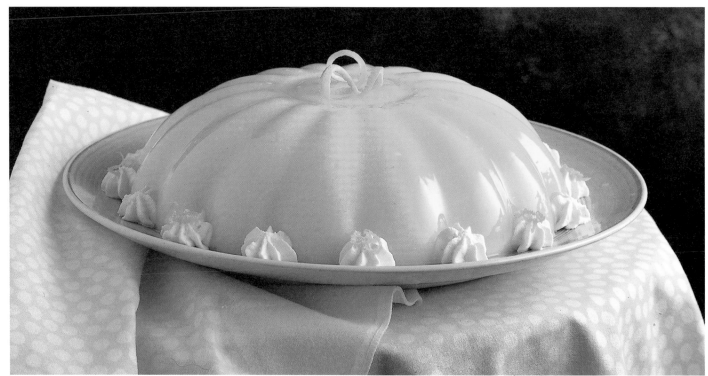

lemon yoghurt jelly

blackcurrant whip

15 minutes + setting	120 kcal/504 kJ per portion

This could also be made with blackcurrants canned in natural juice, in which case omit the sugar and dissolve the gelatine in a little of the juice.

Serves 4

225 g /8 oz frozen blackcurrants, defrosted
300 ml /½ pint natural yoghurt
2 teaspoons powdered gelatine
2 tablespoons water
1 oz caster sugar
2 medium-sized egg whites
20 g /¾ oz blanched almonds

Rub the fruit through a sieve and fold in the yoghurt.
Sprinkle the gelatine over the water in a small bowl. Leave to soak for a few minutes, then place the bowl in a small pan of hot water and heat gently until the gelatine has dissolved. Fold into the blackcurrant purée and add the sugar.
Whisk the egg whites until just stiff, then fold into the blackcurrant purée. Divide between 4 glasses and leave to set.
Before serving, decorate with the almonds.

lemon yoghurt jelly

15 minutes + setting and chilling	235 kcal/987 kJ per portion

This sweet, as shown in the picture, has been decorated and would be suitable for a light ending to a special meal. Without the cream, it would be straight-forward enough for any family meal. Incidentally, whipping cream contains less fat and calories than double cream but is still quite suitable for decoration.

Serves 6

2 packets lemon jelly
300 ml /½ pint natural yoghurt

To decorate:
150 ml /5 fl oz whipping cream
small pieces lemon rind

Put the jelly cubes into a large, heatproof measuring jug. Pour on enough boiling water to make up to 600 ml/1 pint. Stir to dissolve the jelly and leave in a cool place until just beginning to set around the edges.
Add the yoghurt and stir until completely blended. Rinse out a 1.25-litre/2-pint mould with cold water. Pour in the jelly and refrigerate until set.
Shortly before serving, whip the cream stiffly and spoon into a piping bag with a star nozzle.
Turn the jelly out on to a serving plate. Pipe the cream decoratively around the jelly and decorate with the pieces of lemon rind.

honeyed apricot whips

35 minutes
+ soaking
and cooling

130 kcal /546 kJ per
portion

*Dried apricots are both a good source of iron
and of fibre.*

Serves 4

100 g /4 oz dried apricots
300 ml /½ pint hot water
2 tablespoons clear honey
300 ml /½ pint natural yoghurt
2 egg whites

Put the apricots in a small bowl with the hot
water and leave to soak for at least 4 hours,
or, if possible, overnight.
Turn the apricots and water into a
heavy-based saucepan. Add the honey, cover
and simmer very gently for about 20
minutes, until the apricots are tender.
Remove from the heat and leave to cool
completely.
Purée the apricots with the cooking syrup
and yoghurt in a blender. Alternatively, press
the apricots through a nylon sieve, then stir in
the cooking syrup and fold in the yoghurt.
Whisk the egg whites until they stand in soft
peaks. Using a metal spoon, lightly stir 1
tablespoon of the whisked egg whites into
the apricot purée mixture, then fold in the
remainder.
Spoon the whip into stemmed glasses. Serve
at once, or refrigerate until serving time, but
for no more than 1-2 hours.

Serve with: Sponge finger biscuits.

honeyed apricot whips

crunchy apple starter

30 minutes

190 kcal /790 kJ per portion

Serves 4

4 red dessert apples, cored and quartered
2-3 tablespoons lemon juice
2 celery stalks, finely chopped
50 g /2 oz unsalted peanuts
50 g /2 oz shelled hazelnuts
50 g /2 oz sultanas
100 g /4 oz natural yoghurt
1 tablespoon chopped fresh parsley, to
   garnish

Cut each apple quarter lengthways into 2 or
3 slices and toss them in 1 tablespoon of the
lemon juice to prevent them from
discolouring.
Combine all the remaining ingredients,
except the parsley in a small bowl and mix
well. Add lemon juice to taste.
Spoon about half the mixture into 4
individual bowls. Arrange the apple slices on
top to form a rosette shape. Spoon the
remaining mixture into the centre of the
apples and sprinkle a little parsley over each.

crunchy apple starter

pears with blue cheese

10 minutes | 190 kcal/798 kJ per portion

Use this dish as a starter whenever fresh pears are available.

Serves 4

4 thin slices of dark rye bread
25 g/1 oz butter, softened
2 firm dessert pears
2 tablespoons lemon juice
50 g/2 oz Danish blue cheese, cut in slivers
sprigs of watercress, to garnish

Trim the bread to oval shapes a little larger than the pears. Thinly butter one side of each slice.

Peel the pears and halve them lengthways. Scoop out the cores using a teaspoon. Cut a thin sliver off the rounded side of each pear half to make it stand level.

Heat the grill to high. Put the pear halves in a pan of water with the lemon juice. Bring to the boil. Remove the fruit with a slotted spoon, or tip into a sieve to drain. Pat dry on absorbent paper.

Place a pear half, cut side up, on each bread slice. Cover with cheese slivers, making sure the cheese does not hang over the edge. Place the pears, still on the bread, in the grill pan and grill until the cheese bubbles. Put on to individual serving plates and garnish with the watercress. Serve at once.

melon, prawn and grapefruit cocktail

30 minutes + chilling | 175 kcal/735 kJ per portion

Serves 4

2 small Ogen or Charentais melons
1 pink grapefruit
4 tablespoons natural yoghurt
2 tablespoons lemon juice
1 tablespoon caster sugar
salt and freshly ground black pepper
4 tablespoons chopped chives
100 g/4 oz prawns, defrosted if frozen
50 g/2 oz cashew nuts
4 unpeeled prawns, to decorate (optional)

Cut each melon in half horizontally; remove and discard the seeds and seed membrane. With a small melon baller, scoop out as much of the melon flesh as possible into balls and reserve in a bowl. Scrape out the remaining flesh, taking care not to puncture the melon skins, and use for another dish. Place the melon shells in polythene bags and chill.

Peel the grapefruit, taking care to remove every bit of white pith. Cut into segments and remove the seeds with the point of the knife. Cut each segment in half and add to the melon balls. Cover and chill.

Blend the yoghurt with the lemon juice and caster sugar. Season to taste and stir in half the chopped chives.

When ready to serve, drain the melon and grapefruit and toss them in the yoghurt dressing; fold in the peeled prawns, taste and correct the seasoning. Spoon the salad into the chilled melon shells, scatter over the nuts and sprinkle with the remaining chives. Place an unpeeled prawn on each.

Serve with: Thin slices of wholemeal bread.

melon, prawn and grapefruit cocktail

spicy black cherry soup

0·00

1 hour if serving hot + 1 hour if serving cold

170 kcal/714 kJ per portion

An unusual combination of flavours, this soup can be served either hot or cold.

Serves 4

500 g /18 oz black cherries
15 g /½oz butter
1 medium-sized onion, thinly sliced
1 tablespoon flour
900 ml /1½ pints chicken stock
5-cm /2-inch piece of cinnamon stick
2 cloves
2 thinly pared strips of lemon zest
2 egg yolks
50 ml /2 fl oz natural yoghurt

Stone and quarter 16 of the cherries and reserve them for garnish. Stone and chop the rest.
Melt the butter in a saucepan on low heat. Add the onion and cook gently until soft but not browned. Stir in the flour and cook for 1 minute. Stir in the stock and bring to the boil, stirring. Remove from the heat.
Add the chopped cherries, cinnamon, cloves and lemon zest. Bring the soup back to the boil, reduce the heat and simmer gently, uncovered, for 20 minutes.
Strain the soup through a sieve, pressing down hard to extract as much liquid as possible.
Lightly beat the egg yolks together in a bowl and gradually beat 75 ml/3 fl oz of the cherry liquid into them. Mix the contents of the bowl into the rest of the soup and return it to the rinsed saucepan. Reheat gently, without letting it boil.
Pour the soup into individual soup bowls, swirl some yoghurt on top, and scatter over the reserved, quartered cherries to garnish.

prosciutto with melon

0·00

10 minutes

200 kcal/840 kJ per portion

Prosciutto is a delicious cured ham from Italy. Its strong, rich flavour means that only a small amount is needed to provide a satisfying course. To reduce the fat content, it is advisable to cut off and discard the fat around the edge of the meat.

Serves 4

250 g /9 oz prosciutto, thinly sliced
1 Ogen melon

Slice the melon and arrange slices on 4 individual plates. Arrange the prosciutto on the plates with the melon.

prosciutto with figs

0·00

10 minutes

200 kcal/840 kJ per portion

Serves 4

250 g /9 oz prosciutto, thinly sliced
4 ripe figs, quartered

Arrange the quartered figs and the prosciutto on 4 individual plates.

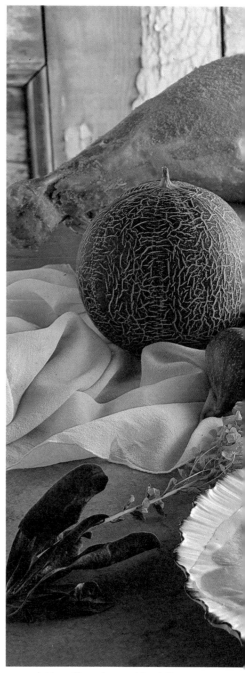

prosciutto with melon and fresh figs

ripe cherry and avocado salad

0·00

30 minutes | 295 kcal /1239 kJ per portion

Serves 4

175 g /6 oz sweet red or black cherries
2 small, ripe avocados
2 tablespoons chopped fresh mint
1 tablespoon chopped fresh tarragon
2 tablespoons oil
1 tablespoon red wine vinegar
freshly ground black pepper
1 small, crisp lettuce
100 g /4 oz curd cheese

Stone the cherries. Peel and stone the avocados and cut them into cubes. Put the cherries and avocado pieces into a bowl with the mint and tarragon.
Mix the oil, vinegar and pepper together and fold this into the cherries and avocados. Make beds of crisp lettuce hearts on 4 small plates and pile a portion of the salad on top of each one. Spoon 25g/1 oz curd cheese on top of each salad and serve immediately to prevent the avocados from discolouring.

prawn and pear salad

0·00

20 minutes | 165 kcal /693 kJ per portion

Serves 4

4 large pears, ripe but still firm
juice of 1 lemon
4 tablespoons calorie-reduced mayonnaise
1 tablespoon tarragon mustard
175 g /6 oz shelled prawns, defrosted if frozen
8 small sprigs of fresh parsley, to garnish

Peel the pears and brush the outsides with lemon juice. Cut each pear in half and remove the core.
Scoop out the centres of the pears, leaving shells about 5 mm /⅛ inch thick. Brush the insides with lemon juice. Chop the scooped-out pieces of pear.
Mix together the mayonnaise and mustard. Stir in the chopped pear and the prawns. Pile the mixture into the pear shells. Arrange 2 halves on each of 4 serving plates and garnish with the parsley.

melon and tangerine salad

melon and tangerine salad

0·00 | **2**

20 minutes | 95 kcal /399 kJ per portion

Serves 4

1 small-to-medium-sized honeydew melon
4 tangerines
1 clove garlic, finely chopped
pinch of salt
1 teaspoon ground ginger
6 tablespoons natural yoghurt
1 lettuce
2 tablespoons sesame seeds

Cut the melon in half, scoop out the seeds and discard. Use a melon baller to make neat balls from the flesh. Otherwise, cut the melon flesh into 15-mm /½-inch cubes. Peel the tangerines, remove the white

membranes and pull into segments. Mix with the melon.
Put the chopped garlic and salt on a plate and crush with a knife until a paste is formed. Mix this and the ginger into the yoghurt. Line a serving bowl with lettuce leaves and pile the melon and tangerine mixture on top. Spoon the yoghurt mixture down the middle and scatter the sesame seeds on top.

cucumber and strawberry salad

0·00 | **2**

15 minutes
+ 30 minutes
for salting
cucumber | 45 kcal /189 kJ per portion

Serves 4

½ cucumber, peeled and thinly sliced
salt
100 g /4 oz strawberries, thinly sliced
   lengthways
sprigs of fennel leaves, to garnish (optional)

For the dressing:
1 tablespoon olive oil
1 tablespoon white wine vinegar
1 teaspoon caster sugar
salt and freshly ground black pepper

Spread the cucumber out on a plate, sprinkle with salt and leave to stand for 30 minutes. Rinse, drain and pat dry.
   Arrange alternate circles of cucumber and strawberries on a flat, round serving plate.
   Make the dressing: put all the dressing ingredients in a screw-top jar with a generous seasoning of salt and pepper. Replace the lid and shake to mix well. Spoon the dressing over the salad, garnish with fennel leaves and serve at once.

haricot beans with stewed apples

1½ hours
+ overnight
soaking

170 kcal /714 kJ per
portion

Serves 4

100 g /4 oz dried haricot beans
450 g /1 lb cooking apples
25 g /1 oz margarine or butter
1 tablespoon clear honey
salt and freshly ground black pepper

Put the haricot beans in a deep bowl, cover with plenty of cold water and leave to soak overnight.

Drain and rinse the beans, put them into a large saucepan and cover with fresh cold water. Bring to the boil, then lower the heat and simmer for about 1 hour or until the beans are tender. Add more water to the pan during the cooking time if necessary. Drain and discard the cooking water.

Peel, quarter and core the apples, then slice thinly. Melt the margarine or butter in a large saucepan, add the apples and cook gently for 10 minutes or until tender. Do not overcook or the apple slices will break up and become browned – they should be very light golden in colour.

Add the haricot beans, honey, and salt and pepper to taste. Cook over very gentle heat for 5 minutes until the beans are warmed through. Turn into a serving dish and serve at once.

Serve with: Pork chops or gammon steaks, or on their own with granary rolls.

haricot beans with stewed apples

lamb with pear stuffing

2¼ hours | 515 kcal /2163 kJ per portion

Serves 6

1.5 kg /3¼ lbs shoulder of lamb, boned
1 tablespoon oil
1 small onion, finely chopped
100 g /4 oz curd cheese
50 g /2 oz fresh wholemeal breadcrumbs
1 large ripe dessert pear, chopped
1 teaspoon chopped fresh tarragon, or
  ½ teaspoon dried tarragon
salt and freshly ground black pepper
1 small egg, beaten
tarragon sprigs, to garnish (optional)

Heat the oven to 170C/325F/Gas 3.
Heat the oil in a small frying-pan. Add the onion and fry gently for 5 minutes until soft and lightly coloured. Using a slotted spoon, transfer to a bowl, add the curd cheese and beat well. Stir in the breadcrumbs, pear and tarragon and season to taste with salt and pepper. Gradually mix in the egg to bind. Lay the lamb skin down on a work surface and spread the cheese mixture over it, pressing down well. Roll up the lamb carefully from one short end and tie at intervals with fine string. Weigh the shoulder of lamb and calculate the cooking time at 30 minutes per 450 g/1 lb plus 30 minutes. Place the lamb in a roasting tin and roast for the calculated time until the juices run clear when pierced with a sharp knife. Leave the lamb in a warm place for 10 minutes to allow it to 'settle' before carving. Transfer to a warmed serving dish and garnish with tarragon sprigs.

Serve with: Boiled new potatoes and a green vegetable in season.

apricot barbecue chicken

55 minutes | 245 kcal /1029 kJ per portion

Serves 4

8 chicken drumsticks, each weighing 100 g /4 oz, skinned
50 g /2 oz toasted almonds, to garnish

For the sauce:
400 g /14 oz can apricots in natural juice
2 tablespoons malt vinegar
2 tablespoons light soy sauce
1 clove garlic
2.5-cm /1-inch piece fresh root ginger, peeled and crushed
salt and freshly ground black pepper

lamb with pear stuffing

Heat the oven to 200C/400F/Gas 6.
Make the sauce: put the apricots and their
juice into a blender, add the remaining sauce
ingredients, with salt and pepper to taste and
work to a rough purée.
Turn the apricot mixture into a saucepan and
bring to the boil. Boil, stirring, for 2-3
minutes until it thickens to a coating
consistency. Fill a roasting tin to a depth of
15-mm/½-inch with cold water and set a rack
over the tin. Arrange the drumsticks on the
rack and brush thickly with half the sauce.
Cook in the oven, on the shelf above centre
for 40-45 minutes until the juices run clear
when the thickest part of the drumsticks is
pierced with a fine skewer. Turn them
occasionally and brush with the sauce.
Transfer the drumsticks to a serving dish and
spoon over any sauce in the tin. Garnish with
the toasted almonds.

herring and apple salad

15 minutes + chilling	230 kcal /966 kJ per portion

Serves 4

4 tablespoons soured cream
150 ml /5 fl oz natural yoghurt
1 large, crisp, red-skinned eating apple
4 pickled herrings, drained and cut into
    2.5-cm /1-inch dice
½ Spanish onion, thinly sliced
salt and freshly ground black pepper

For the garnish:
sprigs of watercress
2 hard-boiled eggs, sliced
snipped chives

In a medium-sized bowl, blend together the
soured cream and yoghurt. Quarter and core
the apple, then cut into thin slices and fold
these into the soured cream mixture. Add the
diced herrings and sliced onion and toss
gently. Season carefully with salt and black
pepper, cover and chill.
Arrange the watercress around the edge of a
serving plate. Toss the salad again, pile it in
the centre and arrange the hard-boiled eggs
around the edge. Sprinkle with chives.

grapefruit cooler

15 minutes
+ 9-10 hours
freezing and
chilling

115 kcal /483 kJ per
portion

Serves 4

grated rind and juice of 2 grapefruit
100 g /4 oz caster sugar
300 ml /½ pint water
2 grapefruit slices, quartered, to decorate

Place the sugar and water in a saucepan and
heat gently until the sugar has dissolved.
Bring to the boil and boil for about 5 minutes,
without stirring, until a thick syrup is formed.

Remove the syrup from the heat and leave
until completely cold. Add the grapefruit rind
and juice to the cold syrup and pour into a
1.25-litres/2-pint shallow freezerproof tin or
ice cube tray without the divisions. Freeze in
the freezer compartment of a refrigerator or
in the freezer for about 30 minutes until
slushy.
Remove from the freezer and stir well with a
metal spoon until evenly blended. Return to
the freezer for 30 minutes, then stir again.
Repeat this process once more, then cover
and freeze for at least 8 hours.
To serve, stir the mixture well, to break up any
large pieces of ice, then spoon into glasses or
small dishes. Decorate each portion with
quartered grapefruit slices. Serve at once.

grapefruit cooler

fruit platter

20 minutes

145 kcal /609 kJ per
portion

Serves 4

2 medium-sized peaches, peeled and sliced
12 large raspberries
3 kiwi fruits, thinly sliced
12 large strawberries
2 medium-sized oranges, skinned, pith
    removed and thinly sliced
1 small honeydew melon, scooped into balls
2 large nectarines, peeled and sliced

For the glaze:
2 tablespoons clear honey
½ tablespoon lemon juice

Arrange the fruit in neat rows by type, on a
large platter. Combine the ingredients for the
glaze and brush over the fruit. Chill until
ready to serve.

fruit drink

5 minutes

60 kcal /252 kJ per
portion

Serves 4

4 oranges
1 small grapefruit
150 ml /5 fl oz fresh pineapple juice

Squeeze the juice from the oranges and
grapefruit. Strain into a jug. Stir in the
pineapple juice, cover and refrigerate until
ready to serve.

fruit platter

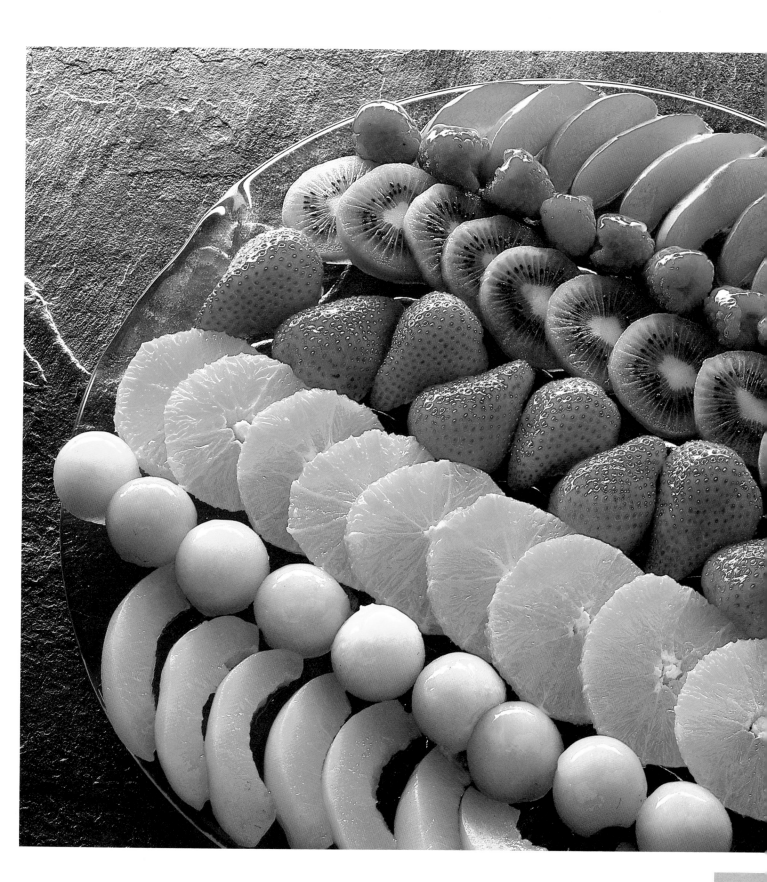

lemon jelly cocktails

0:00

20 minutes
+ 3¼ hours
cooling
and setting

160 kcal/672 kJ per
portion

Serves 4

142 g/5 oz tablet lemon jelly
juice of 1 lemon
boiling water (see recipe)
300 ml/½ pint low-calorie sparkling lemonade
4 maraschino cherries, drained
slices of lemon, to decorate

Place the jelly in a small saucepan. Strain the
lemon juice into a measuring jug and make
up to 150 ml/5 fl oz with boiling water, then
pour on to the jelly.
Stir over very low heat until the jelly has
completely dissolved, then pour the mixture
into a large jug and cool for about 15
minutes.
Refrigerate the jelly for about 1 hour, or until
thickened but still runny. Slowly pour in the
lemonade and stir gently to mix. Pour into 4 x
150 ml/5 fl oz cocktail glasses and return to
the refrigerator for about 1½ hours, or until
almost set.
Spear each cherry on a cocktail stick, then
press gently into each jelly at an angle so that
the cherry lies well below the surface of the
jelly. Refrigerate the jellies for a further 30
minutes, or until set.
Spoon or pipe a swirl of cream on the top of
each jelly, then decorate with lemon slices.
Serve at once.

dried fruit salad

5 minutes
+ 2 days
standing

250 kcal /1050 kJ per
portion

Serves 8

450 g /1 lb dried apricots
225 g /8 oz prunes
100 g /4 oz raisins or sultanas
100 g /4 oz blanched split almonds
50 g /2 oz pistachios, cut in half, or pine nuts
2 tablespoons rose-water or orange blossom
    water

Put all the ingredients together in a large
bowl. Pour in enough water to cover and
leave for at least 48 hours, to allow the fruit
to plump up and the flavours to blend. Serve
the salad with some of the juice.

Serve with: Dollops of thick natural yoghurt.

fresh orange jelly

1 hour
+ 8 hours
setting

125 kcal /525 kJ per
portion

Serves 4

5 large oranges
50 g /2 oz cube sugar
water (see recipe)
5 teaspoons powdered gelatine
1 tablespoon Cointreau or Grand Marnier
    liqueur (optional)
fresh orange slices to decorate

Chill a 600 ml/1 pint metal mould in the
refrigerator. Wash and dry the oranges. Rub
the sugar cubes over the orange skins to
extract the essence from the skin and place
the cubes in a heavy-based saucepan.
Add 100 ml/3½ fl oz water and make a syrup
by stirring over a low heat until the sugar is
completely dissolved. Remove the saucepan
from the heat and reserve.

dried fruit salad

Squeeze the juice from the oranges, strain
and measure out 350 ml/12 fl oz making up
this quantity with a little water if necessary.
Combine the orange juice and sugar syrup,
pour into a jelly bag or muslin-lined sieve and
stand over a clean bowl for about 30 minutes
to let the juice drip through.
Sprinkle the gelatine over 100 ml/3½ fl oz
water in a small pan and leave to soak for 5
minutes. Then set the pan over a very low
heat for 2-3 minutes until the gelatine is
completely dissolved. Remove the pan from
the heat and pour the dissolved gelatine in a
thin stream on to the strained orange juice,
stirring constantly. Stir in the liqueur if using.
Rinse out the chilled mould with cold water
and pour in the orange jelly. Cover and leave
in the refrigerator for about 8 hours or
overnight, until set firm.
To turn out the jelly, wring a cloth out in hot
water and hold it around the mould for a few
seconds, then place a chilled, dampened
serving plate upside down on top of the
mould. Hold the plate and mould firmly and
quickly invert them, giving a sharp jerk
half-way over. When the mould and plate are
completely inverted, give them a firm shake.
Carefully unmould. Arrange the orange slices
in an overlapping circle around the base of
the jelly just before serving.

cambodian fruit salad

`0·00`

35 minutes
+ 2 hours
chilling

80 kcal /336 kJ per
portion (when using
fresh fruit)

Serves 4

1 medium-sized grapefruit, peeled and
    sectioned
1 medium-sized orange, peeled and sectioned
1 small pineapple, peeled, cored and cubed or
    450 g /1 lb canned pineapple cubes in
    natural juice, drained
14 fresh lichees, peeled, stoned and halved, or
    450 g /1 lb canned lichees, drained and
    halved
1 teaspoon lemon or lime juice

Remove any seeds and white pith from the
grapefruit and cut the sections in half.
In a glass bowl, combine the orange and
grapefruit sections with the pineapple and
lichees. Add the lemon or lime juice and mix
lightly. Chill for at least 2 hours before
serving.

blackcurrant sorbet

 0:00

45 minutes
+ 9-10 hours
freezing

 2

120 kcal /504 kJ per
portion

*A tangy and refreshing finish to a meal, that is
quite easy on the calories, too.*

Serves 4

*250 g /9 oz fresh or frozen blackcurrants,
    without stalks
100 g /4 oz caster sugar
300 ml /½ pint water, plus 2 tablespoons
2 teaspoons lemon juice
½ teaspoon powdered gelatine
1 egg white*

Put the sugar and 300ml /½ pint water in a
heavy-based pan and heat gently until the
sugar has dissolved. Boil for 10 minutes, until
turning syrupy, then remove from the heat
and set aside to cool.
Put the blackcurrants into a pan with the
lemon juice and heat gently for about 10
minutes until softened. Cool slightly, then
purée the fruit in a blender. Press the purée
through a sieve.
Sprinkle the gelatine over the 2 tablespoons
water in a small bowl and leave for 5 minutes.
Stand the bowl in a pan of barely simmering
water and stir until the gelatine has
dissolved. Stir this into the sugar syrup. Mix
the sugar syrup with the blackcurrant purée,
blending them together thoroughly. Turn
into a rigid container and freeze for 2-3
hours, until the mixture is firm around the
edges.
Transfer the mixture into a bowl and beat it
thoroughly with a whisk or a fork to break it
up. Whisk the egg white stiffly and fold it into
the blackcurrant mixture. Cover and freeze
until solid.
Let the sorbet stand at room temperature for
15-30 minutes until it is soft enough to scoop
into individual glasses.

Serve with: Small meringues or palmiers.

blackcurrant sorbet

black olive bread

black olive bread

5½ hours

1750 kcal/7350 kJ per loaf

This rather unusual bread is a Greek Cypriot favourite, traditionally eaten on fast days.

makes 1 x 1kg/2¼ lb loaf

25 g/1 oz fresh yeast or 1 tablespoon dried yeast
½ teaspoon brown sugar
tepid water (see recipe)
350 g/12 oz strong wheatmeal flour
½ teaspoon salt
1½ teaspoons olive oil
1 tablespoon oil (any type)
½ large onion, chopped
350 g/12 oz black olives, stoned

In a small bowl, mix the yeast, sugar and 125 ml/4 fl oz tepid water. Stir until the yeast and sugar are dissolved, cover the bowl and leave in a warm place until the yeast is foaming – about 20 minutes.
Sift the flour and salt into a large bowl. Beat in the yeast mixture, the olive oil and enough water to make a fairly stiff, sticky dough. Transfer the dough to a floured board and knead it vigorously until it becomes smooth and elastic and no longer sticks to your fingers – about 15 minutes. Cover with a damp cloth and leave to rise in a warm place until doubled in bulk, about 1½-2½ hours. While the dough is rising, heat the oil in a small frying-pan over medium heat and fry the chopped onion until it is golden brown. Punch down the dough and knead in the fried onion with the oil in which it was cooked, and the olives. Knead the dough until the onion and olives are evenly distributed through it. Shape the dough into a ball and transfer it to an oiled baking sheet. Cover and leave to prove in a warm place until doubled in bulk – 45-60 minutes. Heat the oven to 200C/400F/Gas 6.
Bake the loaf for about 1 hour until golden brown. Remove it from the baking sheet at once and cool by propping it at an angle, so that air can reach all sides. It is best about 3 hours after baking.

Serve with: Greek salad of tomatoes, feta cheese and black olives.

boston brown bread

2½ hours + cooling

170 kcal /714 kJ per portion

An American bread traditionally served with Boston baked beans.

Serves 8

100 g /4 oz rye flour
100 g /4 oz wholemeal flour
100 g /4 oz cornmeal
½ teaspoon bicarbonate of soda
½ teaspoon baking powder
½ teaspoon salt
250 ml /9 fl oz buttermilk
75 ml /3 fl oz molasses

Sift the flours into a mixing bowl with the cornmeal, bicarbonate of soda, baking powder and salt. In a smaller bowl, combine the buttermilk and molasses and stir this liquid into the dry ingredients until just blended.
Pour the mixture into a well-greased 1.2-litre/2-pint pudding bowl. Cover the bowl with greaseproof paper or foil with a pleat to allow for expansion. Steam for 2¼ hours. Turn out the bread and leave to cool. Serve in slices.

Serve with: Home-made baked beans (page 55) or a bean stew.

boston brown bread

boston brown bread

high-fibre bread

1½ hours + 1½ hours rising

1125 kcal /4725 kJ per loaf

makes 2 small loaves

water (see recipe)
1 tablespoon soft light brown sugar
1 tablespoon dried yeast
600 g /1¼ wholemeal flour
100 g /4 oz bran
2 teaspoons salt
1 tablespoon sunflower oil
1 tablespoon kibbled (cracked) wheat

Grease 2 x 900-ml/1½-pint loaf tins and set aside.
Put 325 ml/11 fl oz water into a small bowl and stir in ½ teaspoon sugar and the yeast. Let stand for about 10 minutes, or until frothy. Put the flour, bran, salt and remaining sugar into a large bowl and stir. Make a well in the centre and pour in the yeast mixture, the oil and 200 ml/7 fl oz water. Mix with your hands until a dough is formed, then turn the dough out onto a lightly floured working surface and knead for 5 minutes.
Rinse out the mixing bowl, oil lightly and put the dough into it. Cover with cling film and leave in a warm place for 1 hour, until the dough has doubled in size.
Position an oven shelf in the centre of the oven and heat the oven to 230C/450F/ Gas 8. Punch down the dough with your fist, then knead again for 1-2 minutes. Divide in half and shape each half into a loaf shape the length and width of the tins. Press the top of each loaf in kibbled wheat then put them into the tins, wheat side up, and press the dough well down into the corners.
Cover the loaves with cling film and leave in a warm place for 20-30 minutes or until the dough has reached the top of the tins. Bake for 10 minutes, then reduce the heat to 200C/400F/Gas 6 and bake for a further 25 minutes, until each loaf is crisp and brown and sounds hollow when removed from the tin and tapped on the base. Cool on a wire rack before slicing.

malt fruit loaf

1¾ hours
+ standing,
cooling and
storing

125 kcal/525 kJ per
slice

*A sticky tea bread. Any high fibre bran cereal
will do for this recipe — it can be flakes, grains
or strands.*

makes 10 slices

50 g/2 oz seedless raisins
50 g/2 oz sultanas
50 g/2 oz light soft brown sugar
100 g/4 oz wheat bran breakfast cereal
1 tablespoon malt extract plus extra for
    glazing
300 ml/½ pint skimmed milk
100 g/4 oz self-raising wholemeal flour

Put the raisins, sultanas, sugar, cereal and
malt extract into a large bowl. Pour in the
milk and stir well to mix, then cover and leave
in a cool place for 1 hour, stirring occasionally.
About 20 minutes before the end of the
standing time, heat the oven to
180C/350F/Gas 4. Grease a 450-g/1-lb loaf
tin, line it with greaseproof paper and then
grease the paper.
Uncover the mixture, sift in the flour (adding
any bran left in the sieve) and mix with a
wooden spoon until thoroughly blended.
Turn the mixture into the prepared tin and
bake in the oven for about 1 hour, until risen,
browned and just firm to the touch.
Cool the loaf for 5 minutes, then run a
palette knife around the sides to loosen it,
turn out of the tin and carefully peel off the
lining paper. Place the loaf on a wire rack and
brush the top with malt extract, then leave to
cool completely. Wrap and store in an airtight
container for 24 hours before cutting.

light-weight banana bread

1½ hours

145 kcal/609 kJ per
slice

*This has more 'cake-like' texture than that of
bread. It is a delicious tea-time treat.*

makes 10 slices

65 g/2½ oz margarine
100 g/4 oz soft brown sugar
1 medium-sized egg, beaten
2 small ripe bananas, weighing about 150 g/5
    oz each, mashed
1 tablespoon natural yoghurt
50 g/2 oz wholemeal flour
50 g/2 oz plain flour
½ teaspoon bicarbonate of soda
pinch of salt

Heat the oven to 170C/325F/Gas 3. Cream
the fat with the sugar until light and fluffy.
Beat in the egg until well incorporated. In
another bowl, combine the mashed bananas
with the yoghurt.
Sift the flours, bicarbonate of soda and salt
into a large bowl, adding any bran left in the
sieve. Fold the sifted flour into the creamed
mixture alternately with the mashed
bananas.
Transfer the mixture to a greased 450-g/
1-lb loaf tin and bake in the oven for 1¼ hours.
Remove from the oven and leave to stand in
the tin for 10 minutes before turning out on
to a wire rack to cool.

cheese and caraway biscuits

55 minutes
+ cooling

40 kcal/175 kJ per
biscuit

makes about 20

100 g/4 oz wholemeal flour
¼ teaspoon celery salt
good pinch of dry mustard
50 g/2 oz butter, diced
1 tablespoon grated Parmesan cheese
¼ teaspoon caraway seeds
1 egg yolk
1½ tablespoons water

Heat the oven to 190C/375F/Gas 5 and oil 2
baking sheets.
Sift the flour, celery salt and mustard into a
bowl. Rub in the butter until the mixture
resembles fine breadcrumbs. Stir in the
cheese and caraway seeds.
Mix the egg yolk with the water, and stir into
the flour mixture. Bind together to make a
stiff dough. Turn out on to a lightly floured
surface and knead gently until smooth. Wrap
in cling film and chill for 30 minutes.
Roll out the pastry very thinly on a lightly
floured surface and cut into rounds with a
5-cm/2-inch fluted cutter. Transfer to the
baking sheets.
Bake for 5 minutes, then swap the position of
the baking sheets in the oven and continue to
bake for 5 minutes until crisp and pale
golden. Remove from the oven, allow to
settle for 1-2 minutes, then transfer to a wire
tray with a fish slice and leave to cool.

malt fruit loaf

quick wholemeal bread

1¾ hours

2420 kcal/10164 kJ per loaf

makes 1 large loaf

*700 g/1½ lbs stoneground wholemeal flour
1 tablespoon salt
1½ teaspoons soft brown sugar
1 tablespoon sunflower oil
1½ tablespoons cracked wheat
15 g/½ oz fresh yeast
tepid water (see recipe)*

Sift the flour into a large warm mixing bowl. Stir in the salt and sugar and leave in a warm place for about 5 minutes.
Grease a 1.5-litre/3-pint metal loaf tin with a little of the oil. Sprinkle half the cracked wheat over the base and sides and leave the tin in a warm place.
Blend the yeast with 150 ml/5 fl oz tepid water and pour on to the warmed flour mixture. Add the remaining oil and 300 ml/½ pint tepid water and mix by hand to a moist but manageable dough. If the dough is too stiff, add a little more warm water; if it is too wet, work in extra flour.
Turn the dough out on to a lightly floured surface and knead for 1 minute. Place in the warmed tin and press down evenly with your hand. Sprinkle over the remaining cracked wheat, and press lightly into the dough.
Cover the tin with cling film or a clean, damp cloth; leave in a warm place for 25-35 minutes until the dough has risen just above the top of the tin. Meanwhile, heat the oven to 220C/425F/Gas 7.
Bake the risen bread for 15 minutes; reduce the oven heat to 190C/375F/Gas 5 and bake for a further 25-30 minutes until the bread has shrunk slightly from the sides of the tin. Turn the bread out of the tin and rap the underside smartly with your knuckles: if cooked, it should sound hollow. If necessary, return the bread upside-down to the oven and bake for a few minutes more. Then turn it out on to a wire rack to cool.

quick wholemeal bread

109

spiced thins

1¼ hours + chilling

75 kcal /315 kJ per biscuit

makes 25

225 g /8 oz wholemeal flour
1½ teaspoons ground ginger
1½ teaspoons ground cinnamon
100 g /4 oz margarine or butter, diced
75 g /3 oz light soft brown sugar
1 large egg, lightly beaten

Sift the flour and spices into a bowl. Rub in the margarine or butter until the mixture resembles fine crumbs, then stir in the sugar. Using a round-bladed knife, mix in the egg. Gather the mixture together with your fingers to make a soft dough, turn out on to a lightly floured surface and knead briefly until smooth. Shape into a short roll, 7.5 cm/3 inches in diameter, then wrap in cling film. Put on a plate and refrigerate for at least 2 hours to firm.

Heat the oven to 190C/375F/Gas 5. Lightly oil 2 baking sheets. Unwrap the roll and cut off 5-6 wafer thin slices with a very sharp knife. Place the slices on a baking sheet, spacing them about 4 cm/1½ inches apart to allow for the mixture to spread a little

whilst it is cooking.

Bake in the oven for about 12 minutes, until the edges are lightly browned. Meanwhile, cut another 5-6 slices from the roll and arrange on the second baking sheet. Remove the cooked biscuits from the oven and immediately transfer them to a wire rack to cool and crisp. Bake the second batch of biscuits in the same way as the first. Continue making biscuits, re-oiling the baking sheets as necessary, until all the dough is used.

Serve with: Coffee.

spiced thins

Dissolve the yeast and salt in the tepid water in a large bowl. Stir in the barley flour. Cover the bowl and leave in a warm place for about 30 minutes to 1 hour.

Add the wholemeal flour to the mixture and knead it on a lightly floured surface until smooth. Cover the dough with a tea towel and let it rise for 1 hour or until the dough doubles in bulk.

Punch the dough down and knead it until it is elastic but firm. Form the dough into 2 round loaves. Put them on a lightly greased baking sheet and leave them in a warm place for 1 hour or until they are well puffed up.

Heat the oven to 200C/400F/Gas 6. When the loaves are risen, pierce their tops gently with a fork and bake for 40 minutes or till the bread sounds hollow when you tap the bottom with your knuckles. Cover the bread with a cloth and leave to cool on a wire tray.

minutes. Test the bread with a thin skewer before taking it from the oven to make sure it is done – the skewer should come out clean. Leave the bread 4-6 hours wrapped in a tea-cloth before serving.

Serve with: Soup such as leek and oatmeal soup (see p.68).

oatcakes

30 minutes + cooling

50 kcal/210 kJ per portion

makes about 24

250 g/9 oz fine or medium oatmeal (plus extra for rolling out)
½ teaspoon baking powder
½ teaspoon salt
25 g/1 oz butter

Heat the oven to 200C/400F/Gas 6. Put the oatmeal into a bowl with the baking powder, salt and butter. Mix together lightly, using a fork, then add enough hot water (about 3-4 tablespoons) to make a dough.

Sprinkle some oatmeal on a board and turn the dough on to this; knead it lightly. Roll out to a thickness of 3 mm/⅛-inch and cut into rounds with a pastry cutter. Transfer the oatcakes to a greased baking sheet and bake for about 15 minutes, until firm and lightly coloured. Leave on the sheet for a few minutes, then transfer to a wire rack to cool.

soda bread

1½ hours + 4-6 hours maturing

2600 kcal/10920 kJ per loaf

A traditional Irish bread raised with bicarbonate of soda or baking powder rather than yeast. If you do not have sour milk or buttermilk try using a mixture of natural yoghurt and water, or milk mixed with 2 teaspoons lemon juice.

makes 1 x 1kg/2¼ lb loaf

350 g/12 oz wholemeal flour
350 g/12 oz plain flour
2 teaspoons baking powder
1 teaspoon salt
300 ml/½ pt buttermilk or sour milk
1 medium-sized egg, beaten

Heat the oven to 190C/375F/Gas 5. Sift the flours, baking powder and salt into a large bowl. Beat the buttermilk or sour milk with the egg and stir this into the flour mixture to make a soft, but not slack, dough. Turn out on to a floured surface and knead for a few minutes until the dough is quite smooth. Form the dough into a round shape, then cut a cross about 15-mm/½ inch deep into the top of the loaf. Place the loaf on a lightly greased baking sheet and bake in the oven for 30-40

soda bread

barley bread

4½ hours

1525 kcal/6405 kJ per loaf

makes 2 small loaves

50 g/2 oz yeast
2-3 teaspoons salt
500 ml/18 fl oz tepid water
450 g/1 lb barley flour
300 g/11 oz wholemeal flour

date and walnut loaf

muesli fingers

20 minutes
+ cooling

130 kcal /546 kJ per
biscuit

makes about 16 biscuits

350 g /12 oz unsweetened muesli
4 tablespoons thick honey
4 tablespoons golden syrup
4 tablespoons oil
1 teaspoon ground cinnamon

Heat the oven to 180C/350F/Gas 4.
Put all the ingredients in a bowl and stir well
until thoroughly combined. Press the mixture
into an oiled 28 x 18-cm/11 x 7-inch shallow
tin and bake for 15 minutes.
Leave to cool in the tin for 5 minutes, then
mark into fingers cutting right through the
mixture. Leave until completely cold, then
remove from the tin. Store in an airtight
container; they will keep fresh for weeks.

date and walnut loaf

2¼ hours

200 kcal /840 kJ per
slice

makes 18 slices

225 g /8 oz wholemeal flour
225 g /8 oz plain flour
4 teaspoons baking powder
1 teaspoon salt
½ teaspoon ground mixed spice
75 g /3 oz margarine
50 g /2 oz caster sugar
175 g /6 oz stoned dates, finely chopped
50 g /2 oz walnuts, finely chopped
2 medium-sized eggs, beaten
150 ml /5 fl oz skimmed milk
125 ml /4 fl oz black treacle, warmed

Heat the oven to 180C/350F/Gas 4. Grease
and line a 900-g/2-lb loaf tin.
Sift the flours, baking powder, salt and spice

into a large, warmed mixing bowl, chop in
the margarine and rub in until the mixture
resembles breadcrumbs.
Stir in the sugar, dates and walnuts, then stir
in the beaten eggs and milk. Add the
warmed treacle, a spoonful at a time until the
mixture is a soft, dropping consistency.
Using a spatula, scrape the mixture into the
prepared tin and smooth the top. Bake in the
oven for 2 hours, or until a fine skewer,
inserted into the cake, comes out clean.
Remove from the oven and leave to stand in
the tin for 5 minutes. Turn on to a wire rack,
peel off the lining paper and leave to cool.
Serve in thick slices.

carrot and almond cake

1½ hours | 200 kcal /840 kJ per slice

Serves 8

3 large eggs, separated
2 drops almond flavouring
grated rind of 1 large orange
100 g /4 oz caster sugar
1 tablespoon orange juice
175 g /6 oz carrots, cooked, drained and puréed
100 g /4 oz ground almonds
50 g /2 oz ground rice
15 g /½ oz flaked almonds
15 g /½ oz icing sugar

Heat the oven to 170C/325F/Gas 3.
Generously grease a loose-based, deep, 18-cm/7-inch round tin.
Put the egg yolks, almond flavouring and orange rind in a large bowl and whisk together thoroughly with a hand-held electric whisk. Add the caster sugar, a little at a time, and continue whisking for a further 3-5 minutes, until the mixture is pale and mousse-like.
Whisk in the orange juice and carrot purée, then stir in the ground almonds and ground rice.
In a clean dry bowl and using clean beaters, whisk the egg whites until standing in stiff peaks. Using a large metal spoon, stir one-third of the egg whites into the carrot and almond mixture, then fold in the remainder.
Turn the mixture into the prepared tin, level the surface and sprinkle the flaked almonds around the edge. Bake in the oven just above centre, for 55-60 minutes, until a warmed skewer inserted in the centre comes out clean.
Cool the cake for 15 minutes, then remove from the tin and leave on a wire rack to cool completely. Sift a little icing sugar over the top of the cake before serving.

Serve with: Thick natural yoghurt sweetened with honey.

carrot and almond cake

celebration cake

2¼ hours | 250 kcal /1050 kJ per slice

makes 16 slices

300 g /11 oz wholemeal flour
1 tablespoon baking powder
2 teaspoons ground mixed spice
100 g /4 oz shelled Brazil nuts, chopped
50 g /2 oz dates, chopped
100 g /4 oz Muscovado sugar
125 ml /4 fl oz sunflower oil
175 ml /6 fl oz unsweetened apple juice
350 g /12 oz carrots, grated

To decorate:
15 whole Brazil nuts
8 whole dried dates, halved and stoned
3 tablespoons clear honey.

Heat the oven to 180C/350F/Gas 4. Grease a deep 18-cm/7-inch square cake tin. Line the sides and base with greaseproof paper, then thoroughly grease the lining paper.
Sift the flour into a large bowl with the baking powder and spice. Add any bran left in the sieve and stir well to mix. Stir in the nuts and dates. Add the sugar, oil and apple juice and beat with a wooden spoon until well mixed. Stir in the carrots, mixing well.
Turn the mixture into the prepared cake tin and level the surface. Arrange the Brazil nuts and halved dates in rows over the top. Bake in the oven for about 1¼ hours, or until a fine skewer inserted into the centre of the cake comes out clean. (Cover the cake with greaseproof paper after 30 minutes baking to prevent overbrowning.) Cool the cake for 15 minutes, then turn out of the tin and peel off the lining paper. Place the cake, the right way up, on a large wire rack and brush the top with honey. Leave to cool completely before cutting.

MENU PLANNER

Below are some suggestions for using recipes to produce appetising and nutritious menus as well as balanced meals.

family meals:

Two courses should be ample; choose a simple-to-prepare main course and serve with salad or vegetables followed by a light dessert.

1 Brown rice supper dish (p.72) served with green salad and followed by fresh fruit.
2 Cauliflower, mushroom and oat casserole (p.72), a variation of a family favourite, served with peas and followed by fresh fruit set in jelly.
3 Apricot barbecue chicken (p.98) with baked potatoes and grilled tomatoes, followed by natural yoghurt and chopped apples.
4 Spiced almond beef (p.74) with Chinese cabbage, carrot and beansprout salad (p.48) served with brown rice and followed by grapefruit cooler (p.100).
5 Curried eggs with biriani rice (p.81) with grilled poppadoms, natural yoghurt and sliced bananas, followed by pineapple tinned in natural juice.
6 Home-made baked beans (p.55) with Boston brown bread (p.107), followed by sliced oranges and grapefruits (the vitamin C in the fruit increases the absorption of iron from the beans).
7 Chicken liver bake (p.62) with green vegetables, followed by muesli fingers (p.112) and fresh fruit in season.
8 Barley and bacon hot-pot (p.69) served with mashed potatoes and steamed green cabbage followed by lemon yoghurt jelly (p.90).

light meals and snack meals:

1 Pulse-filled pittas (p.56) followed by fresh fruit.
2 Liver-stuffed tomatoes (p.21) served with wholemeal toast.
3 Leek and oatmeal soup (p.68) served with soda bread (p.111).
4 Tuna and bean salad (p.31) served with wholemeal bread (p.109).
5 Broccoli mustard toasts (p.41) followed by sweet lassi (p.89) (the protein in the drink compensates for the lack of protein in the toasts).
6 Herring and apple salad (p.99) served with wholemeal bread.
7 Baked spinach omelette (p.81) served with baked potatoes and sliced tomatoes.

informal supper parties:

Again two courses will be sufficient when entertaining friends informally and vegetarian dishes can make good and unusual choices.

1 Long pasta with garlic and oil (p.65) served with a green side-salad, followed by dried fruit salad (p.103) and natural yoghurt. (The main course is low in protein, this is compensated for by the nuts in the fruit salad and the yoghurt.)

2 Pork and chick-pea stew (p.17) with baked potatoes and green salad, followed by honey cream (p. 89) with fresh fruit in season.

3 Mixed vegetable curry (p.43) (if you know your guests enjoy curry) with lots of accompaniments — grilled poppadoms, mango chutney, chopped cucumber in yoghurt, sliced bananas, peanuts and plenty of brown rice, followed by fresh orange jelly (p.103).

4 Paella (p.70) followed by blackcurrant whip (p.90).

5 Salmon salad in lemon shells (p.26) followed by nutty rissoles (p.76) tomato sauce, with baked potatoes and steamed broccoli, followed by fresh fruit.

meals for slimmers:

Any of the dishes marked 'low-calorie' are suitable for slimmers but here are a few suggestions for some tasty combinations.

1 Tomato and egg bakes (p.81) for a breakfast dish with a slice of wholemeal toast.

2 Wheaty-pea and vegetable salad (p.73) — a main-course salad, with 1-2 slices of high-fibre bread (p.107). This will fill all hungry gaps.

3 Cottage cheese and chive bakes (p.85) with a wholemeal roll, and fruit.

4 Cucumber and crabmeat salad (p.29) — a tasty main-course salad with 1-2 tablespoons brown rice salad.

5 Beef onions (p.14) with a small baked potato and steamed green vegetables.

6 Entertain slimmers to a meal of Kibbutz citrus carrot salad (p.51) served on a lettuce leaf, followed by poached chicken breasts in cucumber sauce (p.25) with boiled new potatoes and sliced tomatoes sprinkled with freshly ground black pepper, followed by blackcurrant sorbet (p.105).

dinner parties for more formal occasions

An idea here for each season.

Spring: Grapefruit and celery salad (p.53) followed by grilled lemon plaice with almonds (p.36) with duchesse potatoes and steamed carrots, followed by blackcurrant whip (p.90) and sponge fingers.

Summer: Cold seafood platter (p.29) followed by watercress veal (p.20) with new potatoes and broccoli followed by fresh strawberries with honey cream (p.89).

Autumn: Prawn and pear salad (p.96) followed by lamb in red wine (p.19) with courgettes with onions and nuts (p.76) and creamed potatoes followed by cheesecake pots (p.86).

Winter: Prawn bisque (p.27) followed by hazelnut steaks (p.77) with broccoli, raisin and walnut salad (p.41) and baked potatoes followed by honeyed apricot whip (p.91).

Buffets:

Adjust the recipe quantities here to cater for the appropriate number of people.

Summer: Spicy black cherry soup (p.94) and egg mousse (p.82) as starters, followed by cold roast chicken

Poached salmon or jellied tomato and prawn ring (p.27)

Melon and tangerine salad (p.96); yoghurt broad beans (p.45), alfalfa and chicory salad (p.47), potato salad using small new potatoes, parsley and bulgur salad (p.72). Followed by fresh fruit platter (p.100) and honey cream.

Winter: Spinach pâté (p.38); cheese pâté (p.85), and chick-pea dip (p.59) with wholemeal bread

Spiced leg of pork (p.17) and turkey and asparagus apollo (p.24) with two-bean salad (p.57) hazelnut and red cabbage salad (p.79), carrot, fennel and green pepper salad (p.53); beetroot and orange salad (p.51) and warm baked potatoes followed by Cambodian fruit salad (p.104) and coffee served with spiced thins (p.110).

Tea-Parties:

Serve sandwiches made with wholemeal bread (p.109) and filled with: cottage cheese and cucumber, lettuce and tinned salmon, chopped hard-boiled egg and cress. Home-made fruit scones or malt fruit loaf (p.108) or other tea-bread. Carrot and almond cake (p. 113) with thick yoghurt or celebration cake (p. 113) for special tea-parties such as birthdays.

CALORIE CHART

Calorie and kilojoule counts for commonly used foods are given below, together with their high fibre, low fat, low sugar, and low calorie qualities. Use this chart for reference when planning meals.

Food	kcal per 28 g/1 oz	kJ per 28 g/1 oz	High Fibre	Low Fat	Low Sugar	Low Calorie
Almonds, whole or ground, shelled	160	672	✔	–	✔	–
Apples, eating, weighed whole	10	42	✔	✔	✔	✔
Apples, cooking, peeled	10	42	✔	✔	✔	✔
Apricots, dried	52	218	✔	✔	✔	✔
Apricots, fresh, weighed whole	7	29	✔	✔	✔	✔
Artichokes, Globe, boiled	5	21	✔	✔	✔	✔
Artichokes, Jerusalem, boiled	5	21	✔	✔	✔	✔
Asparagus, boiled	5	21	✔	✔	✔	✔
Avocado pear	63	265	–	–	✔	–
Bacon, boiled lean gammon	47	197	–	✔	✔	✔
Bacon, grilled back rashers	115	483	–	–	✔	–
Bacon, grilled streaky rashers	120	504	–	–	✔	–
Baked beans, canned	18	76	✔	✔	–	✔
Banana, raw with skin	13	55	✔	✔	✔	✔
Barley, pearl, raw	102	428	✔	✔	✔	–
Beansprouts	3	13	–	✔	✔	✔
Beef, average lean, raw	35	147	–	✔	✔	✔
Beef, mince, raw	63	265	–	–	✔	–
Beef, roast sirloin, lean	54	227	–	–	✔	✔
Beefburgers, frozen, raw	75	315	–	–	✔	–
Beer, bitter draught, per pint	180	756	–	✔	–	–
Beetroot, boiled	12	50	✔	✔	✔	✔
Biscuits, semi-sweet, average	130	546	–	–	–	–
Biscuits, digestive	134	563	✔	–	–	–
Biscuits, chocolate	140	588	–	–	–	–
Blackberries, raw	8	34	✔	✔	✔	✔
Blackcurrants, raw	8	34	✔	✔	✔	✔
Boiled sweets, average	93	391	–	✔	–	–
Bran, wheat	58	244	✔	✔	✔	✔
Brazil nuts, shelled	175	735	✔	–	✔	–
Bread, brown	63	265	✔	✔	✔	✔
Bread, white	66	277	–	✔	✔	✔
Bread, wholemeal	61	256	✔	✔	✔	✔
Broad beans, boiled	13	55	✔	✔	✔	✔
Broccoli, boiled	5	21	✔	✔	✔	✔
Brussel sprouts, boiled	5	21	–	✔	✔	✔
Butter	210	882	–	–	✔	–
Butter beans, dried	77	323	✔	✔	✔	✔
Butter beans, boiled	27	113	✔	✔	✔	✔
Cabbage, red, white, green, raw	6	25	✔	✔	✔	✔
Carrots, raw	6	25	✔	✔	✔	✔
Cauliflower, raw	4	17	–	✔	✔	✔
Celery, raw	2	8	–	✔	✔	✔
Cheese, Cheddar	115	483	–	–	✔	–
Cheese, cottage	27	113	–	✔	✔	✔
Cheese, cream	124	521	–	–	✔	–
Cheese, Edam	86	361	–	–	✔	–
Cheese, Parmesan	116	487	–	–	✔	–
Cherries, raw, with stones	11	46	✔	✔	✔	✔
Chestnuts, with shells	40	168	✔	✔	✔	✔
Chick peas, dried	91	382	✔	✔	✔	✔
Chicken, roast, meat only	42	176	–	✔	✔	✔

Food	kcal per 28 g/1 oz	kJ per 28 g/1 oz	High Fibre	Low Fat	Low Sugar	Low Calorie
Chicory, raw	3	13	–	✔	✔	✔
Chips, average	72	344	✔	–	✔	–
Chocolate, milk	150	630	–	–	–	–
Chocolate, plain	149	626	–	–	–	–
Cider, average, per pint	200	840	–	✔	–	–
Cocoa powder	88	370	–	–	✔	–
Cod, fresh fillets	22	92	–	✔	✔	✔
Coffee, instant	28	118	–	✔	✔	✔
Corned beef	62	260	–	–	✔	–
Cornflour	100	420	–	✔	✔	–
Crab, canned	23	97	–	✔	✔	✔
Cream, double	127	533	–	–	✔	–
Cream, single or sour	60	252	–	–	✔	–
Cream, whipping	94	395	–	–	✔	–
Crisps	151	634	✔	–	✔	–
Cucumber, raw	3	13	–	✔	✔	✔
Currants, dried	68	286	✔	✔	✔	✔
Damsons, weighed with stones	10	42	✔	✔	✔	✔
Dates, dried	70	294	✔	✔	✔	✔
Duck, roast, meat only	54	227	–	–	✔	–
Eggs, raw with shell	42	176	–	–	✔	✔
Figs, dried	60	252	✔	✔	✔	✔
Flour, white	99	416	–	✔	✔	–
Flour, wholemeal	96	403	✔	✔	✔	–
Gelatine	96	403	–	✔	✔	–
Gooseberries, raw	5	21	✔	✔	✔	✔
Grapefruit, raw, with skin	3	13	–	✔	✔	✔
Grapefruit juice, unsweetened	9	38	–	✔	✔	✔

Food	kcal per 28 g/1 oz	kJ per 28 g/1 oz	High Fibre	Low Fat	Low Sugar	Low Calorie
Grapes, raw, black	14	59	✔	✔	✔	✔
Grapes, raw, white	17	71	✔	✔	✔	✔
Green beans, boiled	5	21	✔	✔	✔	✔
Haddock, raw	21	88	–	✔	✔	✔
Ham, canned, lean	34	143	–	✔	✔	✔
Haricot beans, dried	76	319	✔	✔	✔	✔
Hazel nuts, shelled	107	449	✔	–	✔	–
Herring, raw	66	277	–	✔	–	–
Honey	82	344	–	✔	–	–
Ice-cream, plain	47	197	–	–	–	–
Jam	74	311	–	✔	–	–
Kidney, lamb, raw	26	109	–	✔	✔	✔
Kidney beans, dried	76	319	✔	✔	✔	✔
Lager, average, per pint	160	672	–	✔	–	–
Lamb, lean, raw	46	193	–	✔	✔	✔
Lamb, roast, leg, lean and fat	75	315	–	–	✔	–
Lard	253	1063	–	–	✔	–
Leeks, raw	9	38	✔	✔	✔	✔
Lemon, whole	4	17	–	✔	✔	✔
Lentils, raw, dry	86	361	✔	✔	✔	✔
Lettuce, raw	3	13	–	✔	✔	✔
Liver, lambs, raw	51	214	–	✔	✔	✔
Liver, chicken, raw	38	160	–	✔	✔	✔
Low fat spread	104	437	–	–	✔	–
Mango, raw	17	71	–	✔	✔	✔
Margarine, all types	207	869	–	–	✔	–
Marmalade	74	311	–	✔	–	–
Marrow, raw	4	17	–	✔	✔	✔

Food	kcal per 28 g/1 oz	kJ per 28 g/1 oz	High Fibre	Low Fat	Low Sugar	Low Calorie
Mayonnaise	204	857	–	–	✔	–
Melon, with skin, raw	5	21	–	✔	✔	✔
Milk, whole, cows, per pint	370	1554	–	–	✔	–
Milk, skimmed, fresh, per pint	180	756	–	✔	✔	✔
Mushrooms, raw	3	13	–	✔	✔	✔
Oatmeal, raw	114	479	✔	✔	✔	–
Oil, any type	255	1071	–	–	✔	–
Olives, with stones	23	97	✔	–	✔	–
Onions, raw	7	29	–	✔	✔	✔
Oranges, with skin	8	34	✔	✔	✔	✔
Orange juice, fresh	11	46	–	✔	✔	✔
Parsnips, raw	14	59	✔	✔	✔	✔
Pasta, any shape, raw	105	441	✔ w'meal	✔	✔	–
Peaches, raw, with stones	9	41	✔	✔	✔	✔
Peanuts, shelled	162	680	✔	–	✔	–
Pears, raw	10	42	✔	✔	✔	✔
Peas, fresh or frozen, raw	16	67	✔	✔	✔	✔
Peppers, raw	4	17	–	✔	✔	✔
Pilchards, in tomato sauce	36	151	–	✔	✔	✔
Pineapple, fresh	13	55	✔	✔	✔	✔
Pineapple juice	15	63	–	✔	✔	✔
Plaice, raw	26	109	–	✔	✔	✔
Plums, raw, with stones	7	29	✔	✔	✔	✔
Pork, lean, average	42	176	–	✔	✔	✔
Pork, chops, grilled, lean and fat	73	307	–	✔	✔	–
Potatoes, raw	25	105	✔	✔	✔	✔
Prawns, boiled, shelled	30	126	–	✔	✔	✔
Prunes, dried with stones	38	160	✔	✔	✔	✔

Food	kcal per 28 g/1 oz	kJ per 28 g/1 oz	High Fibre	Low Fat	Low Sugar	Low Calorie
Rabbit, raw	35	147	–	✔	✔	✔
Raisins, dried	70	294	✔	✔	✔	✔
Raspberries, raw	7	29	✔	✔	✔	✔
Rhubarb, raw	2	8	✔	✔	✔	✔
Rice, raw	102	428	✔ brown	✔	✔	–
Rice, boiled	35	147	✔ brown	✔	✔	✔
Salmon, canned	44	229	–	✔	✔	✔
*Sausages, beef, grilled	75	315	–	–	✔	–
*Sausages, pork, grilled	90	378	–	–	✔	–
Shrimps, boiled, shelled	33	139	–	✔	✔	✔
Spinach, boiled	8	34	✔	✔	✔	✔
Strawberries, raw	7	29	✔	✔	✔	✔
Sugar, all types	112	470	–	✔	–	–
Sultanas, dried	71	298	✔	✔	✔	✔
Swedes, raw	21	88	✔	✔	✔	✔
Sweetcorn, canned or frozen	22	92	✔	✔	✔	✔
Tomatoes, raw	4	17	✔	✔	✔	✔
Trout, whole	25	105	–	✔	✔	✔
Turkey, roast, meat only	40	168	–	✔	✔	✔
Turnips, boiled	4	17	✔	✔	✔	✔
Veal, raw fillet	31	130	–	✔	✔	✔
Walnuts, shelled	149	626	–	–	✔	–
Wine, red	19	80	–	✔	–	–
Wine, white, medium	21	88	–	✔	–	–
Yoghurt, fruit, average	27	113	–	✔	–	–
Yoghurt, natural	15	63	–	✔	✔	✔

The calorie counts in this chart first appeared in HMSO's publication *The Composition of Foods*: 4th edition by McCance & Widdowson